It's another winner from the CGP lab...

There are only three ways to make sure you're fully prepared for the new Grade 9-1 GCSE Combined Science exams — practise, practise and practise.

That's why we've packed this brilliant CGP book with realistic exam-style questions for every topic, and we've got all the practicals covered too.

And since you'll be tested on a wide range of topics in the real exams, we've also included sections of mixed questions for Biology, Chemistry and Physics!

CGP — still the best! ☺

Our sole aim here at CGP is to produce the highest quality books — carefully written, immaculately presented and dangerously close to being funny.

Then we work our socks off to get them out to you — at the cheapest possible prices.

Contents

✓ Use the tick boxes to check off the topics you've completed.

Published by CGP

Editors: Mary Falkner, Emily Forsberg, Ciara McGlade, Paul Jordin, Rachael Marshall, Sarah Oxley,
Rachael Rogers, Frances Rooney, Sophie Scott, Hayley Thompson, Sarah Williams.

Contributors: Ian H. Davis, Mark Edwards, Barbara Mascetti, Bethan Parry, Alison Popperwell, Christopher Workman.

With thanks to Charlotte Burrows, Katherine Faudemer, Emily Garrett, Emily Howe and Sarah Pattison for the proofreading.
With thanks to Jan Greenway and Ana Pungartnik for the copyright research.

ISBN: 978 1 78294 498 0

Percentile growth chart on page 17 copyright © 2009 Royal College of Paediatrics and Child Health.

Definition of health in answers to p39: Preamble to the Constitution of the World Health Organization as adopted by the
International Health Conference, New York, 19 June - 22 July 1946; signed on 22 July 1946 by the representatives of 61 States
(Official Records of the World Health Organization, no. 2, p. 100) and entered into force on 7 April 1948.

All references to Warfarin throughout the book are Warfarin™.

Page 82 contains public sector information published by the Health and Safety Executive
and licensed under the Open Government Licence v3.0.
http://www.nationalarchives.gov.uk/doc/open-government-licence/version/3/

Page 160 contains public sector information licensed under the Open Government Licence v3.0.
http://www.nationalarchives.gov.uk/doc/open-government-licence/version/3/

Data used to construct the graph on page 160 provided by the JPL PODAAC, in support of the NASA's MEaSUREs program.

Every effort has been made to locate copyright holders and obtain permission to reproduce sources. For those sources where it has
been difficult to trace the originator of the work, we would be grateful for information. If any copyright holder would like us to make
an amendment to the acknowledgements, please notify us and we will gladly update the book at the next reprint. Thank you.

Clipart from Corel®
Printed by Elanders Ltd, Newcastle upon Tyne

Based on the classic CGP style created by Richard Parsons.

How to Use This Book

- Hold the book <u>upright</u>, approximately <u>50 cm</u> from your face, ensuring that the text looks like <u>this</u>, not ~~s!ɥʇ~~.
  Alternatively, place the book on a <u>horizontal</u> surface (e.g. a table or desk) and sit adjacent to the book,
  at a distance which doesn't make the text too small to read.

- In case of emergency, press the two halves of the book together <u>firmly</u> in order to close.

- Before attempting to use this book, familiarise yourself with the following <u>safety information</u>:

The questions are arranged into sub-topics, so you can get exam practice on exactly the bit of your course that you want.

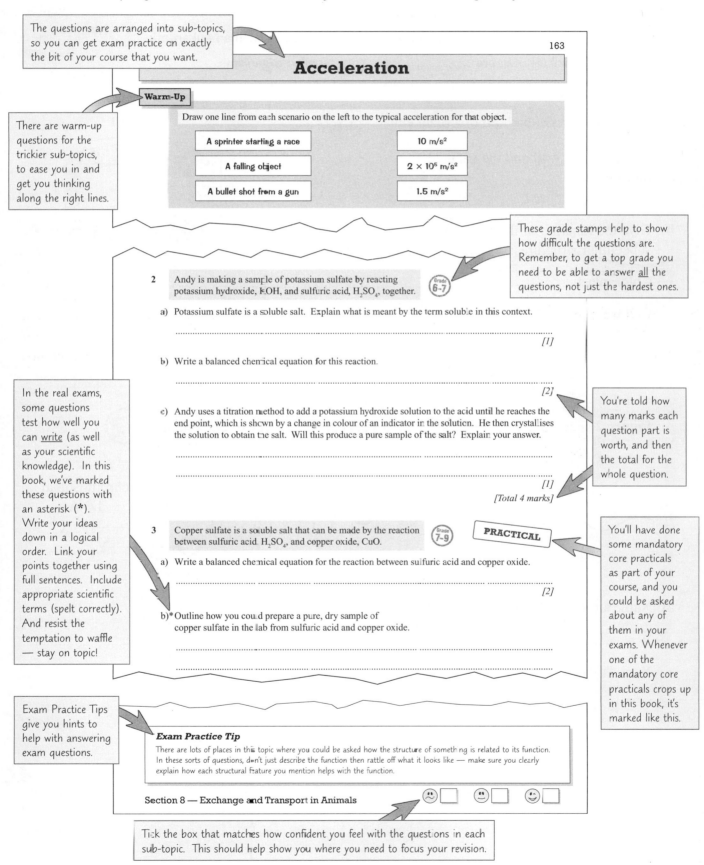

163

Acceleration

Warm-Up

There are warm-up questions for the trickier sub-topics, to ease you in and get you thinking along the right lines.

Draw one line from each scenario on the left to the typical acceleration for that object.

A sprinter starting a race	10 m/s^2
A falling object	$2 \times 10^5 \text{ m/s}^2$
A bullet shot from a gun	1.5 m/s^2

These grade stamps help to show how difficult the questions are. Remember, to get a top grade you need to be able to answer <u>all</u> the questions, not just the hardest ones.

2   Andy is making a sample of potassium sulfate by reacting
    potassium hydroxide, KOH, and sulfuric acid, H_2SO_4, together.   (Grade 6-7)

a) Potassium sulfate is a soluble salt. Explain what is meant by the term soluble in this context.

....

[1]

b) Write a balanced chemical equation for this reaction.

....

[2]

In the real exams, some questions test how well you can <u>write</u> (as well as your scientific knowledge). In this book, we've marked these questions with an asterisk (*). Write your ideas down in a logical order. Link your points together using full sentences. Include appropriate scientific terms (spelt correctly). And resist the temptation to waffle — stay on topic!

c) Andy uses a titration method to add a potassium hydroxide solution to the acid until he reaches the
   end point, which is shown by a change in colour of an indicator in the solution. He then crystallises
   the solution to obtain the salt. Will this produce a pure sample of the salt? Explain your answer.

....

....

[1]

[Total 4 marks]

You're told how many marks each question part is worth, and then the total for the whole question.

3   Copper sulfate is a soluble salt that can be made by the reaction
    between sulfuric acid, H_2SO_4, and copper oxide, CuO.   (Grade 7-9)   **PRACTICAL**

a) Write a balanced chemical equation for the reaction between sulfuric acid and copper oxide.

....

[2]

b)* Outline how you could prepare a pure, dry sample of
    copper sulfate in the lab from sulfuric acid and copper oxide.

....

....

You'll have done some mandatory core practicals as part of your course, and you could be asked about any of them in your exams. Whenever one of the mandatory core practicals crops up in this book, it's marked like this.

Exam Practice Tips give you hints to help with answering exam questions.

Exam Practice Tip
There are lots of places in this topic where you could be asked how the structure of something is related to its function. In these sorts of questions, don't just describe the function then rattle off what it looks like — make sure you clearly explain how each structural feature you mention helps with the function.

Section 8 — Exchange and Transport in Animals   😟 ☐   😐 ☐   😊 ☐

Tick the box that matches how confident you feel with the questions in each sub-topic. This should help show you where you need to focus your revision.

Section 1 — Key Concepts in Biology

Cells

1 **Figure 1** shows a diagram of a plant cell.

Figure 1

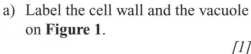

a) Label the cell wall and the vacuole on **Figure 1**.

[1]

b) Give the function of the following subcellular structures:

Chloroplast ....

Cell wall ....

[2]

[Total 3 marks]

2 **Figure 2** shows a diagram of *Pseudomonas aeruginosa*, a type of bacterium.

Figure 2

a) Name structures W, X, and Y on **Figure 2**.

W ....

X ....

Y ....

[3]

b) What is the function of the chromosomal DNA?

....

[1]

[Total 4 marks]

3 Proteins are synthesised within cells. This is done when information from genes is used to join together a sequence of amino acids. The second half of the process is called translation.

Grade 4-6

a) Name **one** subcellular structure where genes are found within:

i) eukaryotic cells.

....

[1]

ii) prokaryotic cells.

....

[1]

b) Name the subcellular structure involved in the translation of genetic material in protein synthesis.

....

[1]

c) Once proteins have been synthesised, they may need to leave the cell.
Name the subcellular structure that controls which substances leave the cell.

....

[1]

[Total 4 marks]

4 **Figure 3** and **4** are diagrams of two different types of specialised cell.
One is a muscle cell and the other is a skin cell. They are not drawn to scale.

Grade 7-9

Figure 4

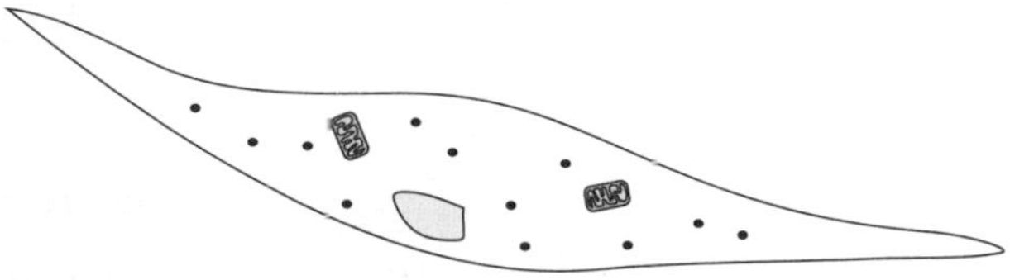

Figure 3

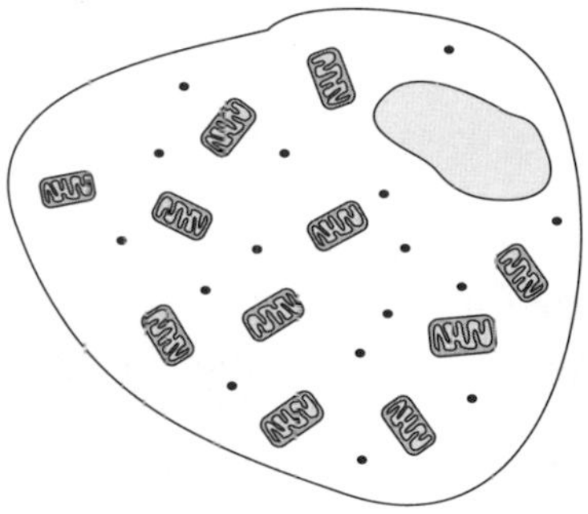

Which cell, **Figure 3** or **Figure 4**, is more likely to be a muscle cell? Explain your answer.

....

....

....

....

[Total 4 marks]

Exam Practice Tip

Make sure you really know the difference between the structures of plant and animal cells (both eukaryotes) and bacterial cells (prokaryotes). Learn all the subcellular structures each one contains and the function of each of those parts — then you should be well-prepared for whatever cell-based questions the examiners throw at you.

Specialised Cells

1   An egg cell is fertilised when the nucleus of an egg cell and the nucleus of a sperm cell fuse together. Both egg cells and sperm cells are haploid.

Grade 4-6

a)   Elephant body cells contain 56 chromosomes.
How many chromosomes will an elephant egg cell contain?

.....................................29...

[1]

b)   Describe the role of a sperm's acrosome in fertilisation.

....

....

[2]

c)   i)   Explain why the membrane of an egg cell changes its structure immediately after fertilisation.

....

....

....

[2]

ii)   Explain how the cytoplasm of an egg cell is adapted to its function.

....

....

[1]

[Total 6 marks]

2   **Figure 1** shows a type of specialised cell which can be found in the lining of the fallopian tubes in the female reproductive system.

Grade 6-7

Figure 1

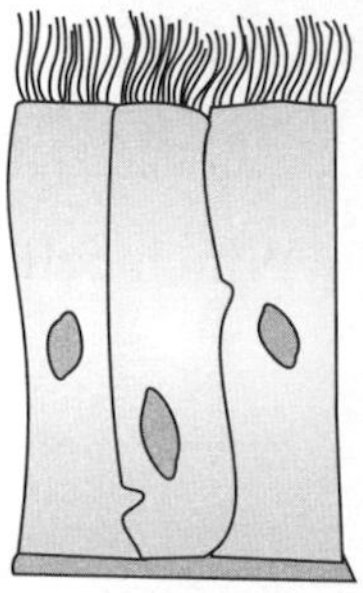

a)   What is the name of this type of cell?

....

[1]

b)   When an egg cell is ready to be fertilised, it moves through the fallopian tubes towards the uterus. Explain how the cells shown in **Figure 1** might be involved in this process.

....

....

....

....

[2]

[Total 3 marks]

Microscopy

1   A student wants to use a light microscope to view a sample of onion cells. **Figure 1** shows a diagram of the light microscope that she plans to use.

Grade 4-6

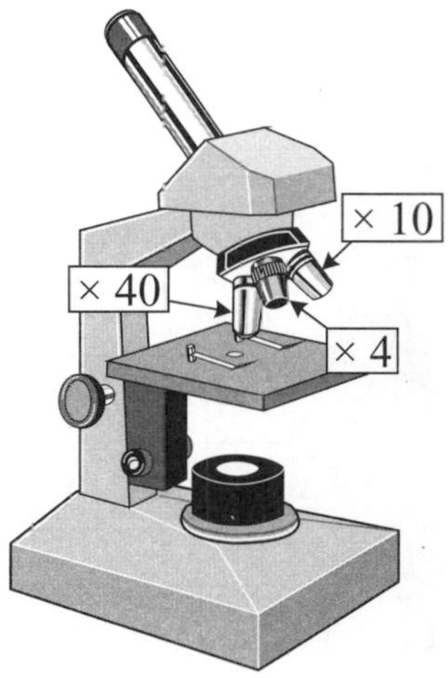

a)   i)   The three different objective lenses are labelled in **Figure 1** with their magnification. Which lens should the student select first when viewing her cells?

....

[1]

Figure 1

× 10

× 40

× 4

ii)   After she has selected the objective lens, she looks down the eyepiece and uses the adjustment knobs. Describe the purpose of the adjustment knobs.

....

....

....

[1]

iii) The student wants to see the cells at a greater magnification. Describe the steps that she should take.

....

....

....

[2]

b)   After she has viewed the cells, she wants to produce a scientific drawing of them. Her teacher has advised her to use smooth lines to draw the structures she can see. Give **two** other ways in which she can ensure she produces an accurate and useful drawing.

1. ....

2. ....

[2]

c)   The student compares the image that she can see with an image of onion cells viewed with an electron microscope. Suggest how the two images would differ. Explain your answer.

....

....

....

....

[3]

[Total 9 marks]

More Microscopy

Warm-Up

1   Fill in the table below to show how the units in the left-hand column are converted into different units and expressed in standard form.

	÷ 1000 will convert to:	× 1000 will convert to:	in standard form, original unit will be:
mm	m	μm	$\times 10^{-3}$ m
μm	mgm	MM	$\times 10^{-6}$ m
nm	μM	μm	$\times 10^{-9}$ m
pm	mm		$\times 10^{-12}$ m

2   Write words in the boxes to correctly complete the following magnification formulae:

total magnification =

| objective | magnification ×
| subjective | magnification

magnification = $\dfrac{\text{image size}}{\text{real size}}$

1   **Figure 1** shows an image of a sample of epithelial cells viewed using a light microscope. An eyepiece lens with a magnification of × 10 and an objective lens with a magnification of × 100 were used to view the cells.

Grade 6-7

Figure 1

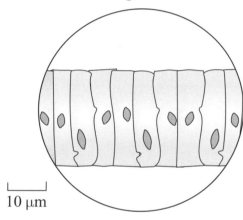

10 μm

a) i) Calculate the total magnification used to view the cells.

total magnification = ...×1000.....

[1]

ii) Estimate the average height of the cells.

average height of the cells = ...25..... μm

[1]

b) A student examines another cell type at the same magnification and finds its average height to be 8 μm. This can be expressed in standard form as

[X] **A** 8×10^{-6} m   [ ] **B** 0.8×10^{-6} m   [ ] **C** 8×10^{-12} m   [ ] **D** 0.8×10^{-12} m

[1]

[Total 3 marks]

2 A student observed blood cells under a microscope.
A scale drawing of one of the cells is shown in **Figure 2**.

Figure 2

A

a) **A** is the cell width. The real width of **A** is 0.012 mm.
Calculate the magnification of the image.

magnification = ...
[2]

b) The cell is then viewed with a magnification of × **400**.
Calculate the new width of the image in mm.

width of image = ... mm
[2]

[Total 4 marks]

3 A plant cell is magnified 1000 times under a light microscope.
The length of the image of the plant cell is 10 mm.

a) Calculate the actual length of the plant cell in μm.

actual length of plant cell = ... μm
[3]

b) An electron microscope is used to look inside the cell in more detail.
A virus particle is noticed that measures 4×10^{-5} mm in width.
Calculate the width of the virus in nm.

.... nm
[3]

[Total 6 marks]

> **Exam Practice Tip**
> Microscopy questions can include some pretty tricky maths. Make sure you learn the magnification formulae and know how to convert from one unit of length to another. Then there's standard form to master — make sure you understand the value of a number written in standard form and can use numbers written in standard form in calculations. Phew.

Section 1 — Key Concepts in Biology

Enzymes

1 Enzymes are biological catalysts. (Grade 4-6)

a) State how a catalyst affects the rate of a reaction.

....

[1]

b) Name the part of an enzyme where substrate molecules bind.

....

[1]

c) Enzymes have a 'high specificity' for their substrate. Describe what this means.

....

....

[1]

[Total 3 marks]

2 The concentration of substrate molecules affects the rate of an enzyme-controlled reaction. (Grade 6-7)

a) Which of the graphs below (**A**, **B**, **C** or **D**) correctly shows how the rate of an enzyme-controlled reaction is affected by substrate concentration?

b) Explain why increasing the substrate concentration fails to affect the rate of an enzyme-controlled reaction after a certain point.

....

....

....

[2]

[Total 3 marks]

3 Temperature affects the rate of enzyme activity. Enzyme A has an optimum temperature of 38 °C. **Figure 1** shows enzyme A before and after being exposed to a temperature of 60 °C.

Figure 1

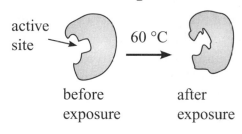

active site → before exposure   60 °C →   after exposure

Enzyme A's activity will be different at 38 °C and 60 °C. Explain why.

....

....

....

....

[Total 3 marks]

4 A scientist investigated the effect of pH on the activity of an enzyme by calculating the rate of reaction for several pH values. His results are shown in **Figure 2**.

Figure 2

pH	3.6	3.8	4.0	4.4	4.8	5.0	5.2
Rate (cm³ s⁻¹)	2.0	5.0	8.0	11.0	8.0	4.0	1.0

a) i) Use the grid in **Figure 3** to draw a graph using the values in **Figure 2**. Include a curve of best fit.

[2]

ii) Determine the optimum pH for this enzyme.

....

[1]

b) Describe and explain the effect on enzyme activity of increasing the pH above the optimum level.

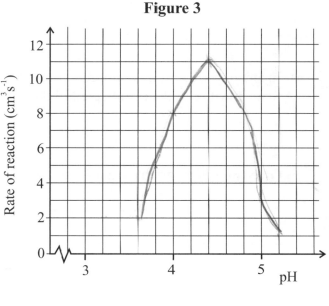

Figure 3

....

....

....

....

[3]

[Total 6 marks]

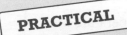

More on Enzymes

1 The enzyme amylase is involved in the breakdown of starch into simple sugars.

A student investigated the effect of pH on the activity of amylase in starch solution. Amylase and starch solution were added to test tubes X, Y and Z. A different buffer solution was added to each test tube. Each buffer solution had a different pH value, as shown in **Figure 1**. Spotting tiles were prepared with a drop of iodine solution in each well. Iodine solution is a browny-orange colour but it turns blue-black in the presence of starch.

Figure 1

Test tube	pH
X	4
Y	6
Z	11

Every 30 seconds a drop of the solution from each of the test tubes was added to a separate well on a spotting tile. The resulting colour of the solution in the well was recorded as shown in **Figure 2**.

Figure 2

Time (s)	30	60	90	120	150
Tube X	Blue-black	Blue-black	Blue-black	Browny-orange	Browny-orange
Tube Y	Blue-black	Browny-orange	Browny-orange	Browny-orange	Browny-orange
Tube Z	Blue-black	Blue-black	Blue-black	Blue-black	Blue-black

a) State the pH at which the rate of reaction was greatest. Explain your answer.

....

....

....

[2]

b) Suggest an explanation for the results in tube **Z**.

....

....

[1]

c) i) In any experiment, it is important to control the variables that are not being tested. State how the student could control the temperature in the test tubes.

....

[1]

ii) Give **two** other variables that should be controlled in this experiment.

1. ....

2. ....

[2]

d) The student repeated her experiment at pH 7 and got the same results as she got for her experiment at pH 6. Describe how she could improve her experiment to find whether the reaction is greatest at pH 6 or 7.

....

....

[1]

[Total 7 marks]

Section 1 — Key Concepts in Biology

Enzymes in Breakdown and Synthesis

1 **Figure 1** shows how different molecules are broken down by enzymes.

Figure 1

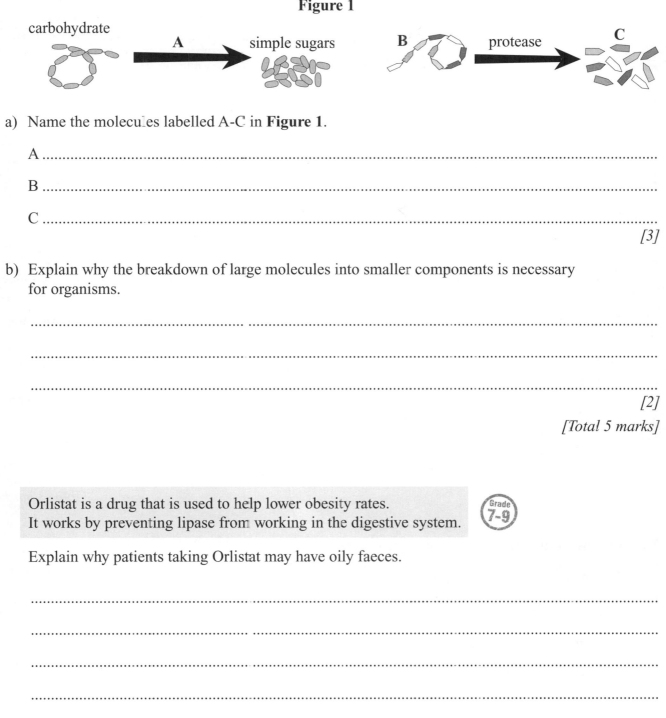

a) Name the molecules labelled A-C in **Figure 1**.

A ....

B ....

C ....

[3]

b) Explain why the breakdown of large molecules into smaller components is necessary for organisms.

....

....

....

[2]

[Total 5 marks]

2 Orlistat is a drug that is used to help lower obesity rates. It works by preventing lipase from working in the digestive system.

Explain why patients taking Orlistat may have oily faeces.

....

....

....

....

....

[Total 3 marks]

Exam Practice Tip

Examiners tend to like asking questions about enzymes — that's because they can make you draw together lots of your knowledge in a single question. For example, you might get asked how temperature affects the breakdown of lipids — you'd need to know that lipases are enzymes which breakdown lipids <u>and</u> how temperature affects enzyme activity.

Diffusion, Osmosis and Active Transport

Warm-Up

The diagram on the right shows three cells. The carbon dioxide concentration inside each cell is shown. Draw arrows between the cells to show in which directions the carbon dioxide will diffuse.

carbon dioxide concentration = 0.2%

carbon dioxide concentration = 1.5%

carbon dioxide concentration = 3.0% ← cell

1 The cell membrane is important in controlling what substances can enter or leave a cell. *(Grade 4-6)*

a) Describe the process of diffusion.

....

....

[2]

b) Which of these types of molecule is too large to diffuse through a cell membrane? Tick **one** box.

☐ **A** protein

☐ **B** oxygen

☐ **C** glucose

☐ **D** water

[1]

[Total 3 marks]

2 Osmosis is a form of diffusion. *(Grade 4-6)*

a) In which **one** of these scenarios is osmosis occurring?

☐ **A** Water is moving from the mouth down into the stomach.

☐ **B** Sugar is being taken up into the blood from the gut.

☐ **C** A plant is absorbing water from the soil.

☐ **D** Oxygen is entering the blood from the lungs.

[1]

b) Give the definition of osmosis.

....

....

....

[3]

[Total 4 marks]

3 Diffusion, osmosis and active transport all involve the movement of molecules.

Grade 6-7

Draw arrows in the boxes underneath **Figure 1** to illustrate the direction of the net movement of the following:

Figure 1

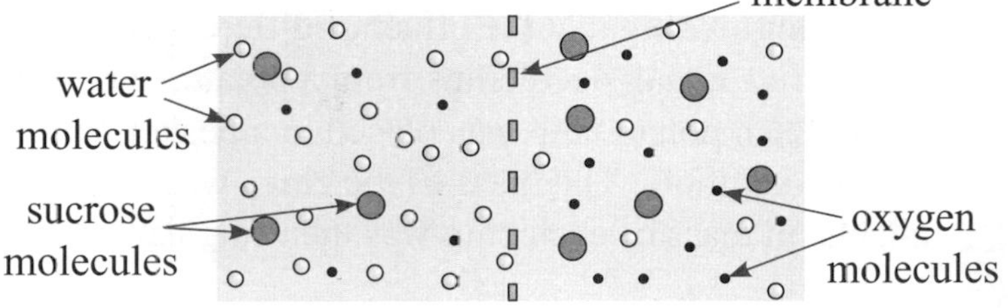

partially permeable membrane

water molecules

sucrose molecules

oxygen molecules

a) sucrose molecules moving by active transport:

[1]

b) water molecules moving by osmosis:

[1]

c) oxygen molecules moving by diffusion:

[1]

[Total 3 marks]

4 Amino acids are absorbed in the gut by active transport. **Figure 2** shows a diagram of amino acids being absorbed into the bloodstream across the epithelial cells of the gut.

Grade 6-7

Figure 2

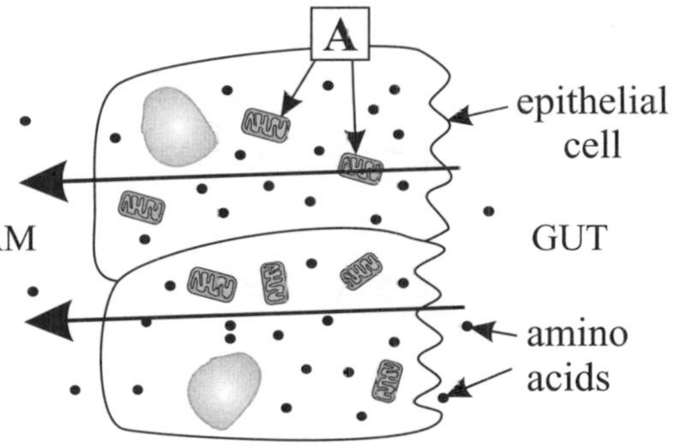

A

epithelial cell

BLOODSTREAM

GUT

amino acids

a) Using **Figure 2**, explain why active transport is necessary for the absorption of amino acids into the bloodstream.

....

....

....

....

[3]

b) Explain why the subcellular structures labelled **A** on **Figure 2** are needed in this process.

....

....

....

[2]

[Total 5 marks]

Section 1 — Key Concepts in Biology

Investigating Osmosis

1   A student investigated the effect of different sucrose solutions on pieces of potato. He cut five equal-sized chips from a potato, and measured and recorded the mass of each. Each potato chip was placed in a beaker containing a different concentration of sucrose solution. The mass of the chips was measured after one hour, and the percentage change in mass of each chip was then calculated. The results are shown in **Figure 1**.

a) The mass of the potato chip in Beaker 5 was 10.0 g before the experiment and 9.3 g afterwards. Calculate the percentage change in mass of the potato chip in Beaker 5.

Figure 1

	Beaker				
	1	2	3	4	5
Concentration of sucrose solution (M)	0.1	0.3	0.5	0.7	0.9
% change in mass of potato chip	9	2	−3	−6	....

Change in mass = ... %

[1]

b) Explain what caused the increase in mass of the potato chips in Beakers 1 and 2.

....

....

[2]

c) Draw a graph of concentration of sucrose solution against percentage change in mass on the grid in **Figure 2**. Include a curve of best fit.

Figure 2

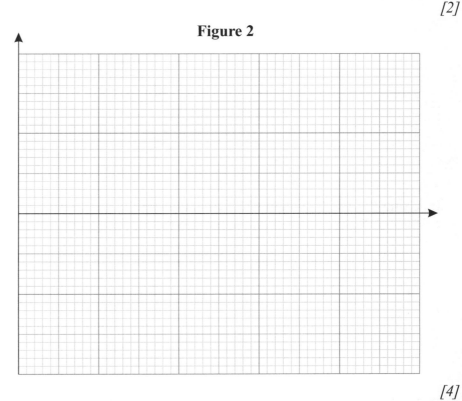

[4]

d) The student wanted to find a concentration of sucrose that would not cause the mass of the potato chip to change. Describe how the student could do this using the graph of the results.

....

....

[1]

[Total 8 marks]

Mitosis

1   Damaged skin tissue can be repaired by mitosis.   (Grade 6-7)

a) Describe what happens in each of these stages of mitosis:

Prophase ....

....

Telophase ....

....

[4]

b) The new skin cells produced by mitosis will be:

☐ **A**   Diploid and genetically identical to each other.

☐ **C**   Diploid and genetically different to each other.

☐ **B**   Haploid and genetically identical to each other.

☐ **D**   Haploid and genetically different to each other.

[1]

c) Other than tissue repair, give **one** reason why an organism's cells divide by mitosis.

....

[1]

[Total 6 marks]

2   Mitosis is part of the cell cycle   (Grade 6-7)

a) Before mitosis occurs, a cell goes through interphase. Describe what happens to the cell's DNA during interphase and explain why this process is necessary.

....

....

[2]

b) **Figure 1** shows a cell undergoing mitosis.

    i) Name the stage of mitosis that the cell is going through.

....

[1]

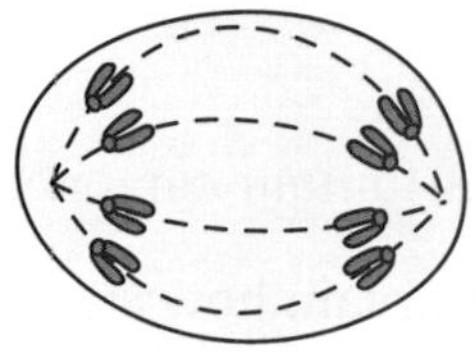

    ii) Describe what is happening during this stage.

Figure 1

....

....

[2]

c) The cell cycle is not complete until cytokinesis has occurred.
Describe what happens during cytokinesis.

....

[1]

[Total 6 marks]

Cell Division and Growth

1 **Figure 1** shows a flowering plant. *(Grade 4-6)*

Figure 1

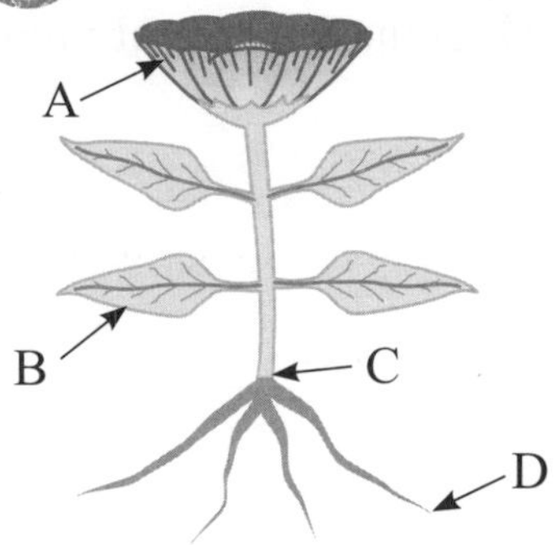

a) Which label (**A-D**) shows a site where growth usually occurs by cell division?

☐ **A**   ☐ **B**   ☐ **C**   ☐ **D**

[1]

b) Name the main process by which plants grow in height.

....

[1]

[Total 2 marks]

2 Animals start life as embryos, which grow and develop. *(Grade 6-7)*

a) State the purpose of cell differentiation in an animal embryo.

....

[1]

b) Describe **two** differences between the growth of animals and the growth of plants.

1. ....

....

2. ....

....

[2]

[Total 3 marks]

3 A tumour can occur in any organ in the body. Not all tumours are cancerous. *(Grade 6-7)*

a) Explain how a tumour forms.

....

....

....

[3]

b) Describe the point at which a tumour is classed as a cancer.

....

[1]

[Total 4 marks]

4 Percentile charts are used to record and monitor a child's growth.   **Grade 7-9**

a) A child's mass was recorded regularly and plotted on the percentile
chart shown in **Figure 2**. The crosses represent the child's mass.

i) Explain what the line labelled '25th'
on the chart represents.

....

....

....

....
[2]

Figure 2

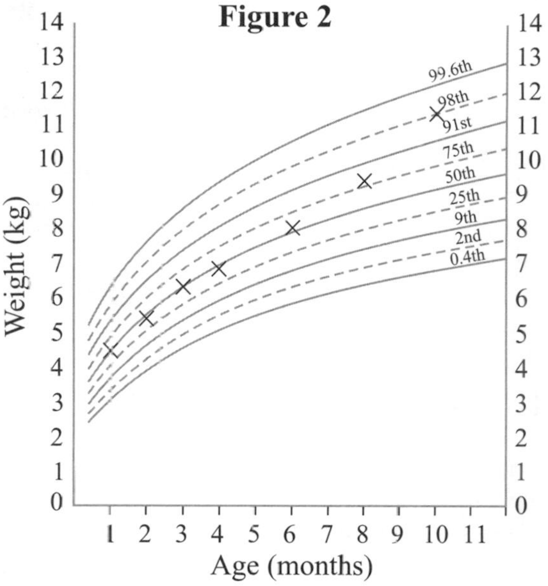

ii) Describe the growth trend shown on the chart
and suggest why a doctor might be concerned
about the child's growth.

....

....

....

....

....
[3]

b) Give **two** other measurements that could be plotted on a percentile chart to monitor growth.

1. ....   2. ....
[2]

[Total 7 marks]

5 **Figure 3** shows the mass of an animal plotted against its age in weeks.   **Grade 7-9**

a) Calculate the rate of growth between 0 and 60 weeks.
Give your answer to 2 significant figures.

Figure 3

rate of growth = ... kg week^{-1}
[2]

b) The animal reaches full growth at
300 weeks. Comment on the amount
of cell differentiation you'd expect to be
occurring at the point marked **X** on the
graph. Explain your answer.

....

....

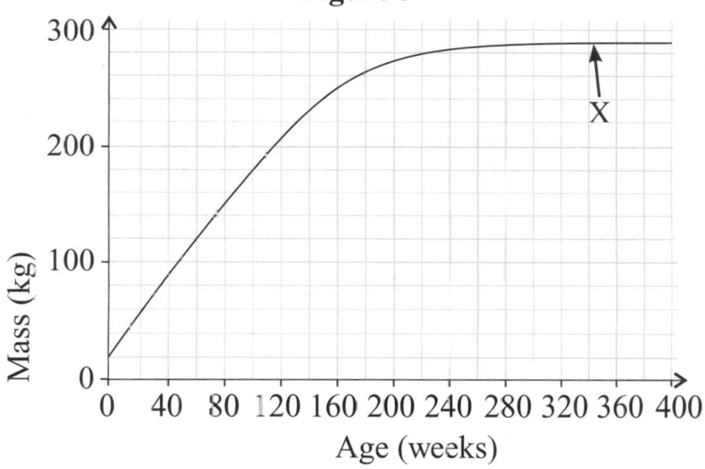

....
[2]

[Total 4 marks]

Section 2 — Cells and Control

Stem Cells

Circle the correct words shown in bold to complete the passage below.

Stem cells are able to **differentiate** / **mutate** to become **specialised** / **unspecialised** cells.

Stem cells found in **adults** / **early human embryos** can produce any type of cell at all.

In plants, stem cells are found in areas of the plant that are **growing** / **photosynthesising**.

Plant stem cells can produce **only a small number of cell types** / **any cell type**.

---

1 Scientists can use stem cells to grow new cells, which they can then use to test new drugs on. **Grade 4-6**

a) Stem cells are

☐ **A** gametes   ☐ **B** specialised   ☐ **C** undifferentiated   ☐ **D** differentiated

[1]

b) i) Explain **one** reason why scientists may prefer to use embryonic stem cells for research rather than adult stem cells.

....

....

[2]

ii) Suggest **one** reason why people are against research involving embryonic stem cells.

....

[1]

c) Scientists can also use plant stem cells in drug research.
Name the plant tissue that produces stem cells.

....

[1]

[Total 5 marks]

---

2 Scientists are researching whether it's possible to use embryonic stem cells to produce insulin-secreting cells, which could potentially be implanted in a patient in order to cure them of type 1 diabetes. **Grade 7-9**

Explain **two** potential risks of using stem cells to cure type 1 diabetes.

....

....

....

....

....

[Total 4 marks]

The Nervous System

Use the words below to complete the following sentences about the nervous system. Each word can only be used once.

motor   sensory   receptors   effectors

The body has lots of sensory .... , which detect environmental stimuli.

When this happens, nervous impulses are sent along .... neurones

to the central nervous system. From the central nervous system, impulses are sent

along .... neurones to .... which produce a response.

---

1 Motor neurone disease occurs when motor neurones stop working as they should. **Grade 7-9**

a) **Figure 1** shows a motor neurone.

Figure 1

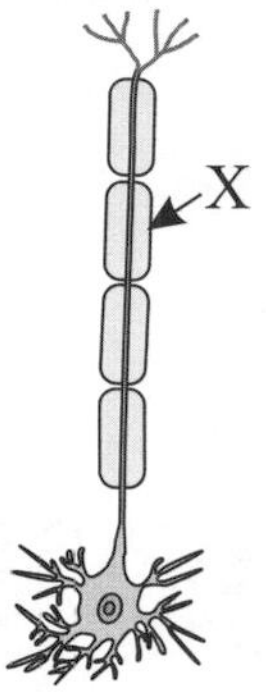

i) Add an arrow to **Figure 1** to show the direction a nervous impulse would travel along the neurone.

[1]

X

ii) Name the part labelled **X** and describe its function.

....

....

[2]

iii) Describe **two** structural differences between a motor neurone and a sensory neurone.

1. ....

....

2. ....

....

[2]

b) Explain why a person with motor neurone disease may have difficulty swallowing.

....

....

[2]

c) A motor neurone is 58 cm long. An impulse travels along it at 110 m s^{-1}.
Calculate how long it would take the impulse to travel the length of the neurone
in milliseconds. Give your answer to 3 significant figures.

.... ms
[3]
[Total 10 marks]

Synapses and Reflexes

1 Humans have many different reflexes. (Grade 4-6)

a) Reflexes are

☐ **A** slow and under conscious control   ☐ **C** rapid and automatic

☐ **B** rapid and under conscious control   ☐ **D** slow and automatic

[1]

b) **Figure 1** shows a diagram of a reflex arc.

Figure 1

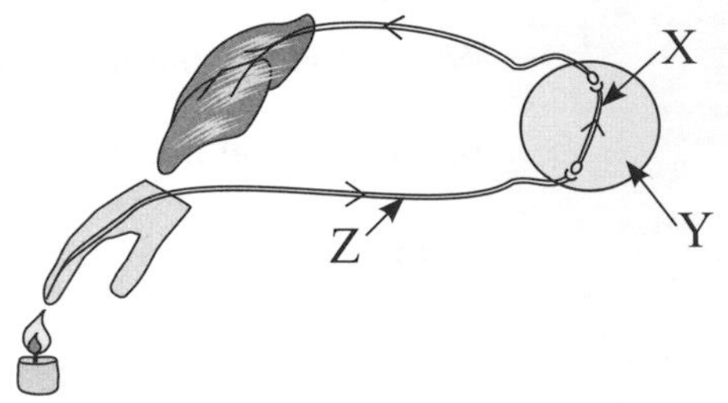

i) Name the structure labelled **X**.

....

[1]

ii) Name **two** parts of the body that the part of the diagram labelled **Y** could represent.

1. ....   2. ....

[2]

iii) Name the structure labelled **Z** and describe its function.

....

....

[2]

iv) State the purpose of the reflex arc shown in **Figure 1**.

....

[1]

[Total 7 marks]

2 Some stimuli are interpreted by the brain as being painful. When receptors detect these stimuli, impulses are passed to the spinal cord and then to the brain. Opioid drugs can relieve pain, partly because they prevent the release of neurotransmitters from certain sensory neurones.

With reference to synapses, explain how opioids can relieve pain. (Grade 7-9)

....

....

....

....

[Total 3 marks]

Exam Practice Tip

The pathway that nervous impulses take in a reflex arc is always the same — receptor, sensory neurone, relay neurone (in the spinal cord or an unconscious part of the brain), motor neurone, effector. Learn this pathway (and understand that synapses connect neurones) then you'll be able to tackle any exam question on reflexes, even if it's a reflex you've not learnt.

Section 2 — Cells and Control

Sexual Reproduction and Meiosis

1   Gametes are produced by meiosis. Human gametes are egg and sperm cells.   *Grade 4-6*

a) Gametes contain...

☐ **A** ...twice as many chromosomes as other body cells.

☐ **B** ...a quarter of the number of chromosomes in other body cells.

☐ **C** ...three times as many chromosomes as other body cells.

☐ **D** ...half the number of chromosomes in other body cells.

[1]

b) Meiosis results in the production of...

☐ **A** ...two genetically identical daughter cells.

☐ **B** ...four genetically identical daughter cells.

☐ **C** ...two genetically different daughter cells.

☐ **D** ...four genetically different daughter cells.

[1]

c) State the name given to the cell formed from two gametes at fertilisation.

....

[1]

[Total 3 marks]

2   **Figure 1** shows a diploid cell about to undergo meiosis.   *Grade 6-7*

Figure 1   **Figure 2**

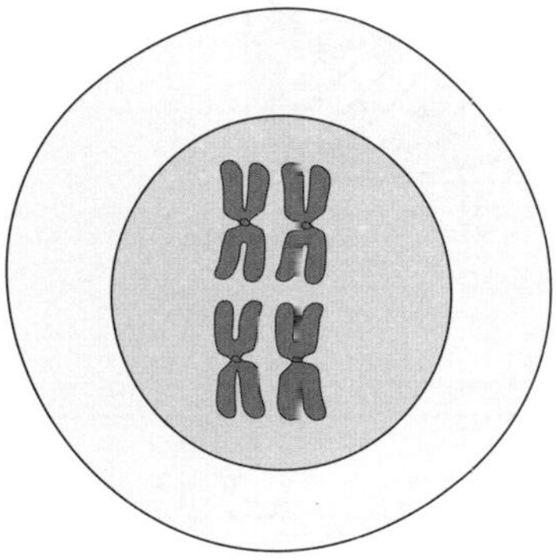

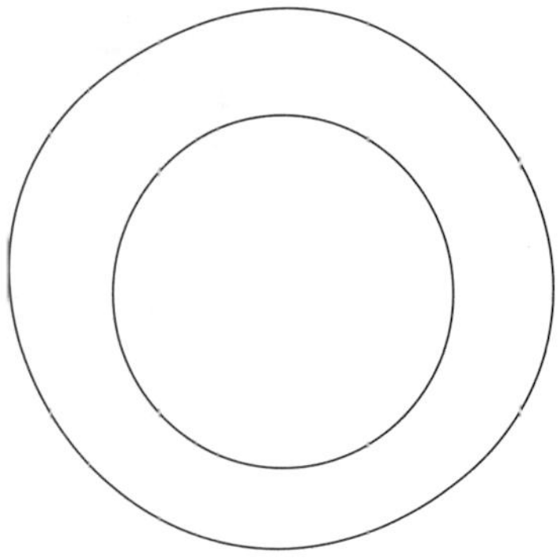

a) Complete **Figure 2** to show the number of chromosomes in a haploid gamete of this organism.

[2]

b) Explain why haploid gametes are necessary for sexual reproduction.

....

....

....

[2]

[Total 4 marks]

☹ ☐   ☺ ☐   ☺ ☐

DNA

1 Scientists have studied the human genome. (Grade 4-6)

a) What is a genome?

☐ **A** All of an organism's DNA.   ☐ **C** All of an organism's genes.

☐ **B** All of an organism's proteins.   ☐ **D** All of an organism's DNA and proteins.

[1]

b) The human genome contains over 20 000 genes.
Explain what is meant by the term 'gene'.

....

....

[1]

c) Describe how DNA is stored in the nucleus of eukaryotic cells.

....

....

[2]

[Total 4 marks]

2 **Figure 1** shows a section of a DNA double helix. (Grade 4-6)

Figure 1

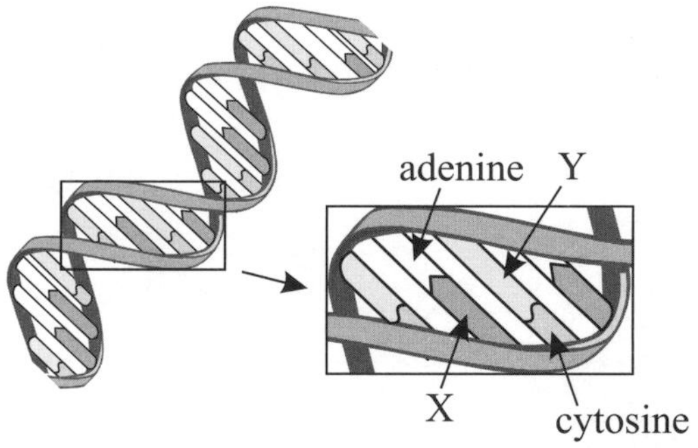

a) Name the bases labelled **X** and **Y** on **Figure 1**.

X: ....

Y: ....

[2]

b) What is meant by the term 'double helix'?

....

[1]

c) DNA is a polymer. Explain what this means.

....

....

[1]

[Total 4 marks]

Section 3 — Genetics

3 A student is extracting DNA from an apple. He begins by breaking up the apple using a food blender. He then adds an 'extraction solution' to the fruit pulp.

Grade 6-7

a) Apart from water, state **two** components of the 'extraction solution'.

1. .... 2. ....

[2]

b) The student filters the mixture into a boiling tube.
Explain what the student needs to do next to obtain a DNA precipitate.

....

....

....

[2]

[Total 4 marks]

4 When a DNA molecule denatures, the bonds between bases on opposite DNA strands break and the two strands separate. **Figure 2** shows how the percentage of denatured DNA in a sample changes as the sample is heated.

Grade 7-9

Figure 2

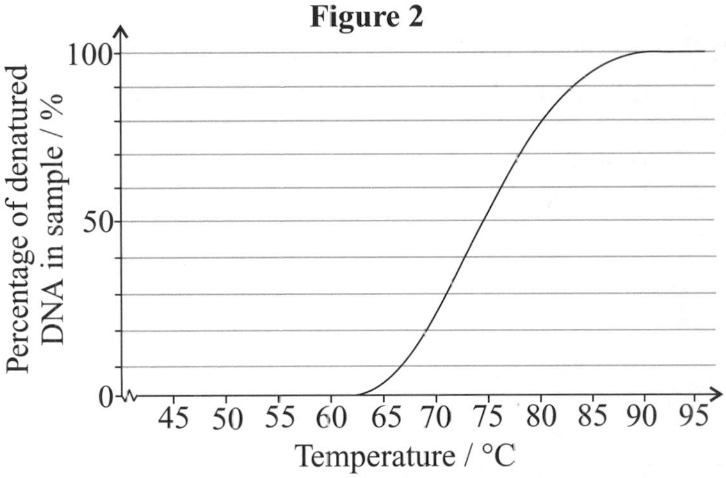

a) Name the bonds that break when a DNA molecule denatures.

....

[1]

b) Give **two** observations that could be made from the data in **Figure 2**.

1. ....

....

2. ....

....

[2]

c) The DNA sample above contains 8.14×10^4 base pairs.
Calculate how many base pairs have separated at 70 °C.
Give your answer in standard form to 3 significant figures.

.... base pairs

[2]

[Total 5 marks]

Genetic Diagrams

Draw lines to match the words on the left to the correct definition on the right.

genotype   Having two alleles the same for a particular gene.

phenotype   The combination of alleles an organism has.

allele   The characteristics an organism has.

heterozygous   Having two different alleles for a particular gene.

homozygous   A version of a gene.

1   Height in pea plants is controlled by a single gene. The allele for
    tall plants (T) is dominant over the allele for dwarf plants (t).

    Grade 4-6

    A student says that a pea plant must have the genotype TT to be tall.
    Is the student correct? Explain your answer.

    ....

    ....

    [Total 2 marks]

2   Polled cattle have no horns. The polled allele (N) is dominant over the
    allele for horns (n). A farmer wants to breed a herd of polled cattle.

    Grade 6-7

a) The farmer breeds a polled bull with
    a horned cow. Both the bull and the
    cow are homozygous for their trait.

    Complete the Punnett square on the right
    to show the genotypes of the offspring.

	....	....
....	....	....
....	....	....

    [1]

b) The farmer later breeds a heterozygous polled bull with several heterozygous polled cows.
    Give the likely ratio of polled cattle : horned cattle in the calves.
    Draw a genetic diagram to explain your answer.

    ratio of polled calves : horned calves ....

    [2]

    [Total 3 marks]

3 **Figure 1** shows a tabby cat. Tabby cats have a distinctive banding pattern on their fur. The banding is controlled by a single gene. The allele for banding (B) is dominant over the allele for solid colour fur (b).

Figure 1

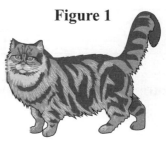

a) State the **two** possible genotypes for the cat shown in **Figure 1**.

1. .... 2. ....

[2]

b) A heterozygous tabby cat breeds with a cat with solid-colour fur.

i) Draw a genetic diagram to show the probability of one of the offspring being a tabby.

probability of one of the offspring being a tabby: ....

[2]

ii) The heterozygous tabby and the cat with solid-colour fur have 6 kittens. State how many of these kittens are likely to be tabby.

....

[1]

[Total 5 marks]

4 Hair length in Syrian hamsters is controlled by a single gene. The allele for short hair (H) is dominant over the allele for long hair (h).

Explain how a breeder could determine the genotype of a short-haired hamster.

....

....

....

....

....

....

[Total 4 marks]

Exam Practice Tip

You've really got to learn all the scientific words related to this topic (dominant, recessive, homozygous, etc.). Not only could you be asked to define them in the exam, it's assumed you'll know what the terms mean when they're used in questions. It's hard to get the right answer if you don't know what the question's asking you, so get learning that vocab.

More Genetic Diagrams

1   **Figure 1** shows how the gender of offspring is determined.

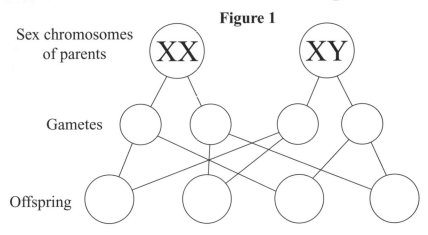

Figure 1

Sex chromosomes of parents

Gametes

Offspring

a) Complete **Figure 1** to show the sex chromosomes of the gametes and the offspring.

[1]

b) Give the ratio of male to female offspring. ....

[1]

[Total 2 marks]

2   PKU is a genetic disorder caused by a recessive allele (h). **Figure 2** shows a family pedigree for a family in which one of the children has PKU.

Figure 2

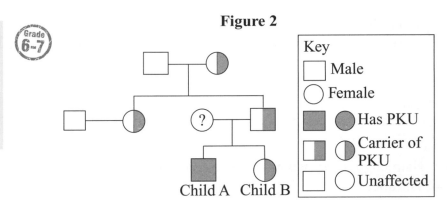

a) i) State the genotype of child A. ....

[1]

ii) State the **two** possible genotypes of Child A's mother.

1. ....   2. ....

[2]

b) Two carriers of PKU have a child.
Complete the Punnett square to show the
percentage probability that they will have a
child who does **not** have the disorder.

	....	....
....	....	....
....	....	....

probability of having a child who does not have the disorder: ....%

[2]

[Total 5 marks]

Variation

1   Mutations can have different effects on the phenotype of an organism.   *(Grade 4-6)*

a)   Explain what is meant by the term 'phenotype'.

....

[1]

b)   Which **one** of the following statements is true?

☐   **A**   A single mutation usually has a large effect on an organism's phenotype.

☐   **B**   Most mutations affect an organism's phenotype, but only slightly.

☐   **C**   Most mutations have no effect on an organism's phenotype.

☐   **D**   A single mutation never has any effect on an organism's phenotype.

[1]

[Total 2 marks]

2   An experiment was carried out into the causes of variation in plant height. Three different controlled environments (A, B and C) were set up. Five plants of the same species were grown from seed in each environment. The heights of all the plants were measured after six weeks and are shown in **Figure 1**.   *(Grade 6-7)*

Figure 1

Plant height / cm (y-axis)

Environment (x-axis: A, B, C)

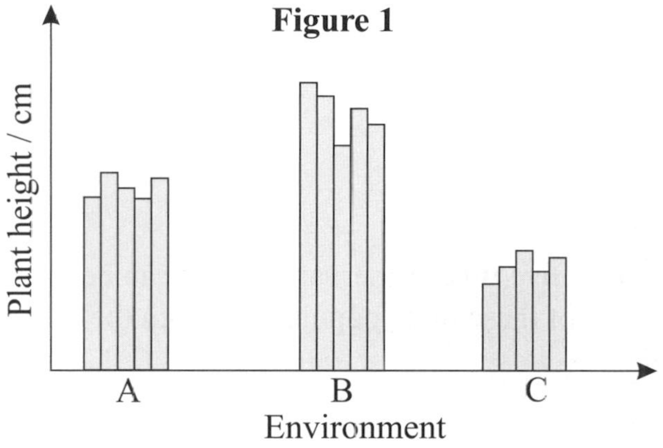

a)   Some variation in plants is genetic and can be caused by mutations.
Give **one** other cause of genetic variation within a plant species.

....

[1]

b)   Some variation in plants can be caused by the environment.
What name is given to a characteristic caused by environmental variation?

☐   **A**   an assisted characteristic   ☐   **C**   an additional characteristic

☐   **B**   an acquired characteristic   ☐   **D**   an advanced characteristic

[1]

c)   Using the information in **Figure 1**, explain whether variation in plant height in this species is caused by genes, the environment or both.

....

....

....

....

[4]

[Total 6 marks]

Section 3 — Genetics

3 The heterozygosity index (H) can be used to measure the genetic variation in a population. H always has a value between 0 and 1. The closer the value to 1, the more alleles there are in the population. **Figure 2** shows the value of H for three different populations of the same species in two different years. The populations reproduce via sexual reproduction.

Figure 2

	Population 1	Population 2	Population 3
Value of H in 2005	0.42	0.41	0.48
Value of H in 2015	0.43	0.40	0.52

a) Calculate the difference in the mean value of H for the three populations, between 2005 and 2015.

Difference in mean value: ....

[3]

b) Give **three** observations that can be made about the genetic variation of these three populations from the data in **Figure 2**.

1. ....

....

2. ....

....

3. ....

....

[3]

c) Would you expect the population of an organism that only reproduces via asexual reproduction to have a higher or lower value of H than the populations shown in **Figure 2**? Explain your answer.

....

....

....

....

[2]

[Total 8 marks]

The Human Genome Project

1   Scientists hope to be able to use knowledge gained from the Human Genome Project to improve the treatment of disease.   **Grade 6-7**

a)   Outline the aim of the Human Genome Project.

....

....

[1]

b)   Describe **one** way in which knowledge gained from the Human Genome Project and related research could help scientists to develop new and better medicines.

....

....

[1]

c)   Explain **one** way in which the Human Genome Project has affected the testing or treatment of inherited disorders.

....

....

....

....

[2]

[Total 4 marks]

2   Some genetic variants have been discovered that are associated with an increased risk of developing late onset Alzheimer's disease. However, there are currently no medically approved genetic tests for these variants.   **Grade 6-7**

a)   Explain **one** possible benefit of testing a person for genetic variants that are associated with an increased risk of developing Alzheimer's disease later in life.

....

....

....

[2]

b)   Give **two** possible drawbacks of testing a person for these genetic variants.

1. ....

....

2. ....

....

[2]

[Total 4 marks]

Section 3 — Genetics

Natural Selection and Evidence for Evolution

Fill in the blanks in the paragraph below using some of the words on the right.

Natural selection describes how .... alleles become more common in a population. Selection pressures such as .... and .... mean that not all organisms will survive and reproduce. Individuals with alleles that make them better .... their environment are more likely to survive and pass on their alleles to their ....

predation
beneficial
survival
competition
offspring
used to
adapted to
stronger

1 Organisms can only adapt to their environment if there is genetic variation in the population.

Grade 4-6

a) Individuals in a population show genetic variation because of differences in their:

☐ **A** selection pressures   ☐ **C** cells

☐ **B** alleles   ☐ **D** adaptations

[1]

b) How do new alleles arise in a population of organisms?

....

[1]

[Total 2 marks]

2 Bacteria can quickly evolve resistance to a particular antibiotic.

Grade 6-7

a) Suggest **one** reason why bacteria can evolve quickly.

....

[1]

b) Explain how a bacterium could become less affected by a particular antibiotic.

....

[1]

c) i) State the selection pressure involved when bacteria develop resistance to an antibiotic.

....

[1]

ii) Explain how antibiotic resistance becomes more common in a population over time.

....

....

....

[3]

[Total 6 marks]

3 Warfarin™ is an anti-blood-clotting drug. It can be used as a poison to kill rats. Some rat populations have evolved to become resistant to Warfarin.

Grade 7-9

a) Explain **one** benefit to the rats of developing resistance to Warfarin.

....

....

[2]

b) **Figure 1** shows how the percentage of Warfarin-resistant rats in a population changed after the introduction of Warfarin as a rat poison. Explain how this data provides evidence for evolution.

....

....

....

....

....

....

....

....

....

[4]

[Total 6 marks]

Figure 1

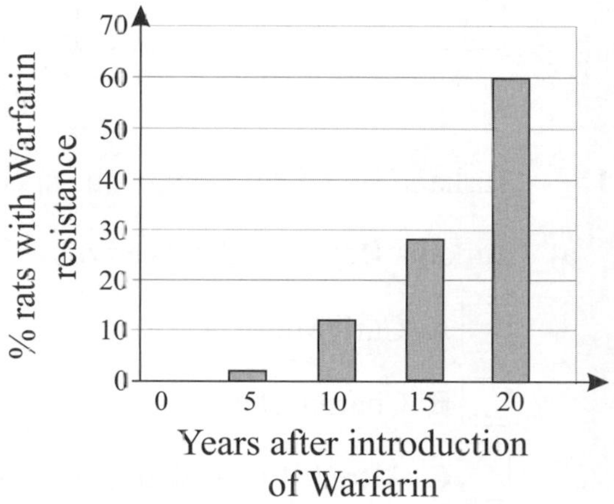

% rats with Warfarin resistance

Years after introduction of Warfarin

4* A population of finches on an island mainly eat seeds. The finches vary in the size of their beaks. Larger beaks are better for breaking apart larger seeds, whereas smaller beaks are better for picking up and eating smaller seeds. A storm kills off many of the plants that produce larger seeds.

Grade 7-9

Describe how evolution by natural selection may lead to a change in the beak size in the population of finches, following the storm.

....

....

....

....

....

....

....

....

[Total 6 marks]

Exam Practice Tip

Natural selection is a big favourite with examiners, so make sure you learn it well. If you get asked about natural selection in a context you haven't heard of before, don't panic — the process always involves the same steps in the same order. You just need to apply what you know to the information you're given in the question.

Fossil Evidence for Human Evolution

Show the age of the fossils on the right by putting the correct name into each of the boxes on the timeline below.

'Lucy'   'Ardi'

'Turkana Boy'

million years ago

5   4   3   2   1   0

---

1 'Turkana Boy' is a fossil of the species *Homo erectus*.   Grade 4-6

a) 'Turkana Boy' was discovered by the scientist:

[ ] **A** Carl Woese

[ ] **B** Charles Darwin

[ ] **C** Alfred Russel Wallace

[ ] **D** Richard Leakey

[1]

b) Give **two** features of the 'Turkana Boy' skeleton, which suggest that his species was more human-like than the species of 'Ardi' or 'Lucy'.

1. ....

2. ....

[2]

[Total 3 marks]

---

2 Human ancestors began using stone tools around 2.6 million years ago. Being able to date stone tools allows scientists to see how they developed over time.   Grade 6-7

Figure 1

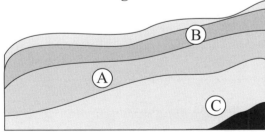

a) i) **Figure 1** shows the distribution of three stone tools (A-C) across the layers of rock at a fossil site. Put the stone tools in most likely order of age, from oldest to youngest.

....

[1]

ii) Apart from studying the layers of rock that the tools are found in, give **two** methods that a scientist could use to date the stone tools at this fossil site.

1. ....

2. ....

[2]

b) Explain how stone tools provide evidence for the evolution of the brain in human ancestors.

....

....

....

[2]

[Total 5 marks]

---

3 An anthropologist is comparing a number of skeletons of human ancestors. He estimates their brain sizes using their skull remains. His results are shown in **Figure 1**. **Figure 2** shows a timeline for the evolutionary history of some human ancestor species.

Grade 6-7

Figure 1

Specimen	1	2	3
Brain size (cm³)	950	325	457

Figure 2

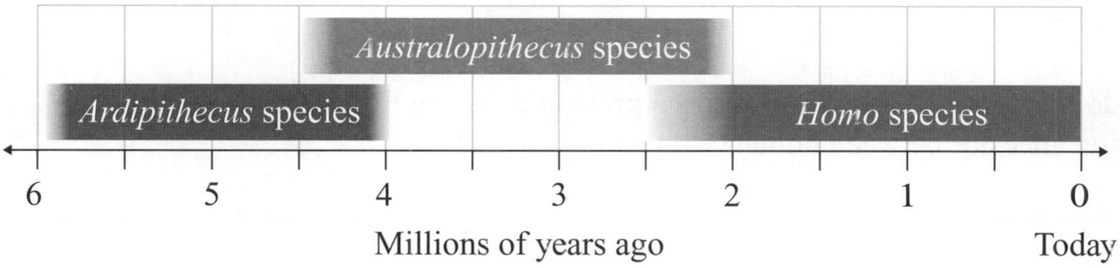

a) Use **Figures 1** and **2** to determine which specimen (1, 2 or 3) is:

i) a *Homo* species ....

ii) an *Australopithecus* species ....

iii) an *Ardipithecus* species ....

[2]

b) Evidence suggests that species from further back in **Figure 2** were generally shorter in height than the more recent species. Suggest a physical reason for this.

....

[1]

[Total 3 marks]

Section 4 — Natural Selection and Genetic Modification

4   Hominids are humans and their ancestors. Fossil hominids provide evidence for the evolutionary relationship between humans and apes.

Figure 3 shows the bone structure of a chimpanzee foot. Chimpanzees are apes. It also shows the foot bones of two incomplete fossil hominids and the bone structure of a human foot. Fossil A is older than fossil B.

Figure 3

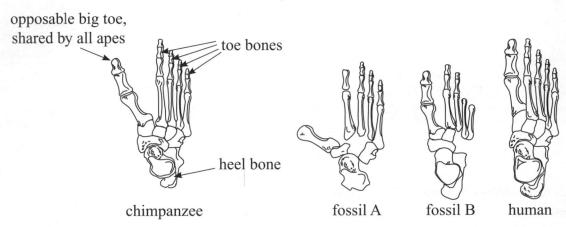

opposable big toe, shared by all apes

toe bones

heel bone

chimpanzee   fossil A   fossil B   human

a) i) Using **Figure 3**, give **one** feature shared by **fossil A** and the chimpanzee, which is not found in humans.

....

[1]

ii) Suggest an explanation for why this feature is not found in humans.

....

....

[2]

b) How do the hominid fossils in **Figure 3** provide evidence for a shared common ancestor between humans and chimpanzees?

....

....

[1]

c) **Fossil B** belongs to the same species as the fossil 'Lucy'.
    Other than differences in the foot structure, describe **one** difference you would expect to find between fossil B's skeleton and a chimpanzee's skeleton.

....

....

[1]

[Total 5 marks]

Exam Practice Tip

Make sure you know how features in our hominid ancestors changed over the course of evolutionary history.
As hominids evolved to be more like humans and less like apes, legs became longer, arms became shorter and brains increased in size. Feet also become more adapted to walking than climbing trees.

Classification

1 Classification involves arranging living organisms into groups. In one system of classification, organisms are first arranged into five groups called kingdoms.

Grade 4-6

a) Write down the five kingdoms in this classification system.

....

[1]

b) What is the correct order of the following groups in the five kingdom classification system, from biggest to smallest?

☐ **A** kingdom, phylum, class, order, family, species, genus

☐ **B** kingdom, family, order, class, phylum, species, genus

☐ **C** kingdom, phylum, genus, species, class, family, order

☐ **D** kingdom, phylum, class, order, family, genus, species

[1]

[Total 2 marks]

2 Nowadays, the three domain classification system is widely used to classify organisms. One of the domains is Eukarya.

Grade 4-6

a) Fungi are part of the Eukarya domain.
State **three** other types of organism in the Eukarya domain.

....

[1]

b) Name the other **two** domains in the three domain system.

....

[2]

[Total 3 marks]

3 Changes in technology and chemical analyses led to the development of the three domain classification system in 1977.

Grade 6-7

a) Explain how DNA sequencing techniques can be used to determine relationships between organisms.

....

....

....

[2]

b) Explain how genetic analysis led to the prokaryote kingdom being split into two domains.

....

....

....

[2]

[Total 4 marks]

 ☐ ☐ ☐

Section 4 — Natural Selection and Genetic Modification

Selective Breeding

1 Selective breeding can be used to produce organisms with characteristics that are useful to humans.

Grade 4-6

a) Suggest **two** uses of selective breeding in agriculture.

1. ....

2. ....

[2]

b) Suggest **one** use of selective breeding in medical research.

....

[1]

[Total 3 marks]

2 A farmer discovers that some of his dairy cows produce a little more milk per day than the rest of his herd.

Grade 7-9

a) Explain the steps that the farmer could take to breed a herd of cows with high milk yields from his existing herd.

....

....

....

....

....

[3]

b) Weaver Syndrome is a genetic defect found in dairy cows. After successfully breeding cows with high milk yields, the farmer notices that more of his cows have Weaver Syndrome than in his previous herd. Suggest a reason for this.

....

....

....

[2]

c) Explain why the emergence of an infectious disease, such as bovine tuberculosis, may be more of an issue for the farmer's new herd than for his previous herd.

....

....

....

....

[3]

[Total 8 marks]

Section 4 — Natural Selection and Genetic Modification

Genetic Engineering

Warm-Up

Draw lines to connect each word or phrase on the
left with the statement describing it on the right.

restriction enzyme	a type of vector
plasmid	cuts DNA open
ligase	an organism with DNA from a different species
GM organism	sticks DNA ends together
vector	transfers DNA into a cell

1   Genetic engineering involves modifying the genome of one
organism by introducing a gene from another organism.

Grade 6-7

a) i) Outline how a desired gene would be isolated from an organism.

....

....
[1]

ii) Explain how a vector can be used to insert the gene into a bacterial cell.

....

....

....

....
[3]

b) Which of these is an example of a vector used in genetic engineering?

☐ **A** a hybridoma

☐ **B** a virus

☐ **C** a glucose molecule

☐ **D** a protein
[1]

c) Explain **one** advantage of being able to insert the gene for a desired protein into a bacterial cell.

....

....
[2]

[Total 7 marks]

2   Genetically modified corn plants are grown in
many parts of the world due to their pest resistance.

Grade 6-7

a) Apart from pest resistance, give another example of a beneficial characteristic that could be
introduced into a crop by genetic modification.

....

[1]

b) Give **two** reasons why some people may have concerns about the use of
genetically modified crops in agriculture.

1. ....

....

2. ....

....

[2]

[Total 3 marks]

3*   A scientist discovers that she is able to genetically modify
hens to produce particular proteins in the whites of their eggs.

Grade 7-9

Discuss the potential advantages of the scientist's findings in medicine and other areas,
and also the concerns that some people may have over genetically engineering animals.

....

....

....

....

....

....

....

....

....

....

[Total 6 marks]

Exam Practice Tip

Make sure you know plenty of arguments both for and against genetic engineering — they're the sort of thing examiners
love to ask about. And don't forget the basic principles of using vectors and enzymes to genetically modify an organism
— the techniques may vary a little depending on whether it's an animal/plant etc., but the basic idea is still the same.

Health and Disease

Warm-Up

Write the type of pathogen that causes each of the diseases below, using the words on the right. You may use a word more than once, or not at all.

Chalara ash dieback ....

Tuberculosis ....

Malaria ....

Cholera ....

protist

virus

fungus

bacterium

1   The World Health Organisation (WHO) monitors the health of people worldwide and coordinates research into communicable and non-communicable diseases.   (Grade 4-6)

a) Give the WHO's definition of health.

....

....

[2]

b) Describe the difference between a communicable and a non-communicable disease.

....

....

[1]

[Total 3 marks]

2   Tuberculosis is caused by a pathogen.   (Grade 4-6)

a) Describe how the pathogen that causes tuberculosis is spread between individuals.

....

....

[1]

b) Give **one** effect of tuberculosis on the human body.

....

[1]

c) Describe **one** way in which the spread of the pathogen that causes tuberculosis may be reduced.

....

....

[1]

[Total 3 marks]

3 Chalara ash dieback disease was originally noticed in ash trees in Poland in the 1990s. In 2012, a case of ash dieback was diagnosed in Britain, and it is now very widespread.

(Grade 6-7)

a) Give **two** symptoms of chalara ash dieback disease.

....

[2]

b) Suggest **one** way in which the disease may have been transmitted from Poland to Britain.

....

[1]

c) Describe **one** precaution that could be taken to limit any further spread of the disease.

....

....

[1]

[Total 4 marks]

4* Malaria is caused by a microorganism called *Plasmodium*. *Plasmodium* can only cause malaria if it is able to complete its growth cycle, which can only happen if temperatures are high enough. In many countries affected by malaria, climate change is leading to an increase in temperature at higher altitudes, where malaria was not previously present.

(Grade 7-9)

Explain why it may be advisable for people in high altitude areas of countries affected by malaria to learn how to use mosquito nets.

....

....

....

....

....

....

....

....

....

....

....

....

[Total 6 marks]

Exam Practice Tip

There are a lot of communicable diseases that you need to know about for the exam. Make sure you know the pathogen that causes each one, the effects it causes, how it is spread and how its transmission can be prevented. Take the time to learn them all properly — if you get them mixed up in the exam you could be throwing away marks.

Section 5 — Health, Disease & the Development of Medicines

STIs

1 *Chlamydia* is a disease which may result in infertility.   Grade 4-6

a) Name the type of pathogen that causes *Chlamydia*.

....

[1]

b) State how *Chlamydia* is most commonly transmitted between individuals.

....

[1]

c) i) The National Chlamydia Screening Programme was set up to reduce the spread of *Chlamydia* in the UK. Explain **one** reason why screening individuals without symptoms could help to reduce the spread of the disease.

....

....

....

[2]

ii) Give **one** additional method for preventing the spread of *Chlamydia*.

....

[1]

[Total 5 marks]

2 HIV is a virus that eventually leads to AIDS in the people it infects.   Grade 6-7

a) Explain why a person with AIDS may become seriously ill due to infection by another pathogen.

....

....

....

[2]

b) Suggest an explanation as to why, in order to protect themselves from HIV, drug users should not share needles.

....

....

....

[2]

[Total 4 marks]

Fighting Disease

1 The body has many features which it can use to protect itself against pathogens. *(Grade 4-6)*

a) Give **one** example of a physical barrier against pathogens in humans.

....
[1]

b) What is the name of the enzyme present in tears which kills bacteria on the surface of the eye?

  ☐ **A** carbohydrase   ☐ **B** protease   ☐ **C** amylase   ☐ **D** lysozyme
[1]

c) Name the chemical which kills most pathogens that reach the stomach.

....
[1]

[Total 3 marks]

2 B-lymphocytes are a type of white blood cell involved in the specific immune response. *(Grade 6-7)*

a) State what is meant by the term 'specific immune response'.

....
[1]

b) Explain how B-lymphocytes help the body to fight against invading pathogens.

....

....

....

....

....
[4]

[Total 5 marks]

3 Primary cilia dyskinesia (PCD) is a disease in which cilia don't work properly.
Suggest an explanation as to why people with PCD are likely to get frequent lung infections. *(Grade 7-9)*

....

....

....

....

....

[Total 3 marks]

Memory Lymphocytes and Immunisation

1 Antibodies are important proteins in the immune response to a pathogen. **Figure 1** shows how the concentration of a particular antibody in the blood of a person changes over time. *(Grade 6-7)*

a) At which point on the graph (**A**, **B**, **C** or **D**) are memory lymphocytes first produced?

☐ A

☐ B

☐ C

☐ D

[1]

Figure 1

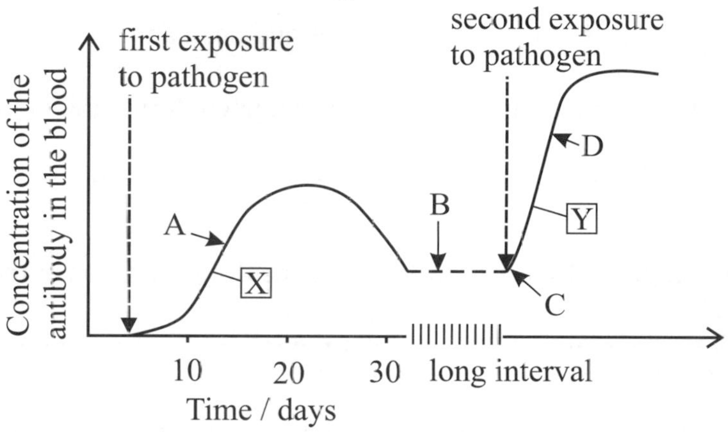

first exposure to pathogen

second exposure to pathogen

Concentration of the antibody in the blood

A

X

B

Y

D

C

10   20   30   long interval

Time / days

b) Explain why the curve on **Figure 1** labelled **Y** is steeper than the curve labelled **X**.

....

....

....

....

....

[3]

[Total 4 marks]

2 In 1988 the World Health Organisation began a global immunisation programme to try to eradicate polio. *(Grade 7-9)*

a) Before being used in immunisation, the virus which causes polio is first treated with a chemical called formaldehyde. Suggest a reason for this.

....

[1]

b) Explain why a person who has been immunised against polio would be less likely to develop the disease if the virus entered their body.

....

....

....

....

....

[3]

[Total 4 marks]

      Section 5 — Health, Disease & the Development of Medicines

Antibiotics and Other Medicines

1   New drugs have to undergo pre-clinical and clinical testing before they can be used.   **Grade 4-6**

a) i) Preclinical testing is carried out on:

☐ **A** healthy human volunteers   ☐ **C** patients in a hospital

☐ **B** human cells, tissues and dead animals   ☐ **D** human cells, tissues and live animals

[1]

ii) Give **one** thing which is investigated during the pre-clinical testing of drugs.

....

[1]

b) Suggest why very low doses of the drug are given at the start of clinical trials.

....

[1]

c) Placebos and double-blind methods are often used in clinical trials.

i) Explain why placebos are used.

....

....

[1]

ii) Explain why double-blind trials are used.

....

....

[1]

[Total 5 marks]

2   Antibiotics are used to cure many different diseases.   **Grade 6-7**

a) Explain why antibiotics can be used to treat bacterial pathogens in humans.

....

....

[2]

b) Antibiotics are not effective against viruses.
Suggest an explanation as to why it is difficult to develop drugs that target viral pathogens.

....

....

....

[2]

[Total 4 marks]

Non-Communicable Diseases

1 Non-communicable diseases are not spread by pathogens, instead they are associated with risk factors.

Grade 4-6

a) Describe what is meant by a 'risk factor' for a disease.

....

....

[1]

b) Describe how drinking too much alcohol can cause liver disease.

....

....

[2]

c) Give **one** disease which is associated with smoking.

....

[1]

[Total 4 marks]

2* Being overweight or obese in childhood is an important risk factor for developing obesity as an adult. One of the main aims of the UK government's Change4Life campaign is to tackle childhood obesity.

Grade 7-9

Explain which lifestyle factors Change4Life is likely to tackle and the economical reasons why the government may have developed this campaign.

....

....

....

....

....

....

....

....

....

....

[Total 6 marks]

Exam Practice Tip

Think carefully about 6 mark questions like the one on this page. Don't just start scribbling everything you know about the topic. Stop and think first — work out what the question is wanting you to write about, and then make sure you write enough points to bag yourself as many marks as possible. Good job you've got some practice on this page...

   Section 5 — Health, Disease & the Development of Medicines

Measures of Obesity

1   A woman decides to lose weight by reducing her calorie intake. She is 170 cm tall and before she starts to reduce her calorie intake she has a mass of 73.5 kg. Her waist circumference is 91 cm and her hips circumference is 84 cm.

Grade 6-7

a) Calculate her waist-to-hip ratio.
Give your answer to 2 significant figures.

waist-to-hip ratio = ...
[1]

b) **Figure 1** shows weight descriptions for a range of BMI values.

Figure 1

i) Calculate her BMI before she starts to reduce her calorie intake. Give your answer to 3 significant figures.

Body Mass Index	Weight Description
below 18.5	underweight
18.5 - 24.9	normal
25 - 29.9	overweight
30 - 40	moderately obese
above 40	severely obese

BMI = ...kg m^{-2}
[3]

ii) After six months of her reduced calorie intake her BMI is calculated as 19. Using **Figure 1**, explain why her doctor advised her to consider increasing her calorie intake again.

....
[1]

[Total 5 marks]

2   Patients at a health centre had their BMI and waist-to-hip ratios calculated as part of a survey. The results of five of the patients are shown in **Figure 2**. A waist-to-hip ratio over 1 in men and over 0.85 in women indicates obesity.

Grade 7-9

a) Using **Figure 2**, explain which patient (**A-E**) is most at risk of developing cardiovascular disease.

Figure 2

Patient	Sex	BMI	Waist-to-hip ratio
A	Female	19.2	0.9
B	Male	26.1	0.9
C	Female	30.3	1.2
D	Female	30.5	0.7
E	Male	30.6	1.0

....
....
....
[2]

b) **Patient D** is a fitness instructor. Explain why her BMI may be misleading when assessing her risk of developing obesity-related disorders.

....
....
....
[2]

[Total 4 marks]

Treatments for Cardiovascular Disease

Warm-Up

Use the correct words to fill in the gaps in the passage. Not all of them will be used.

asthma   cystic fibrosis   arteries

heart   lungs   respiration rate   veins   strokes   blood pressure

Cardiovascular disease is a term used to describe diseases of the blood vessels and

.... A high level of cholesterol in the blood and a high

.... can lead to cardiovascular disease by causing fatty

deposits to build up in .... This restricts blood flow,

which can lead to problems such as ....

---

1 Doctors were assessing the heart of a patient who had recently suffered from a heart attack. They noticed that one of the main arteries supplying the heart muscle was narrowed.

Grade 6-7

a) Give **two** pieces of lifestyle advice the doctors are likely to give to the patient.

1. ....

2. ....

[2]

b) The doctors tell the patient he could have a surgical procedure to reduce the chance of having another heart attack.

i) Explain how a surgical procedure could improve the patient's condition.

....

....

[2]

ii) If the patient decides to go ahead with surgery, give **two** risks he should be made aware of.

1. ....

2. ....

[2]

c) Give **two** examples of medication that the patient could take to improve his condition. Explain what each medication does.

1. ....

....

2. ....

....

[4]

[Total 10 marks]

  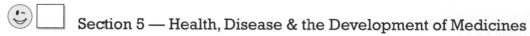

Section 5 — Health, Disease & the Development of Medicines

Photosynthesis

Warm-Up

Complete the following passage using words on the right. You do not need to use all the words.

Photosynthesis is carried out by organisms such as green plants
and .... It uses energy transferred by
.... to produce ....
This energy is absorbed by subcellular structures called
....

mitochondria

glucose algae

fungi chloroplasts

minerals

fructose

light

1 Photosynthesis is a chemical reaction, which allows
photosynthetic organisms to generate their own food source.

Grade 4-6

a) Complete the word equation for photosynthesis.

.... + ... → .... + ...

[1]

b) Photosynthesis is an endothermic reaction. This means that:

☐ **A** energy is taken in during the reaction.

☐ **B** energy is transferred to the surroundings during the reaction.

☐ **C** energy is made during the reaction.

☐ **D** energy is broken down during the reaction.

[1]

[Total 2 marks]

2 The sugar produced in photosynthesis can be broken
down to transfer energy as part of respiration in a plant.

Grade 6-7

a) Give **one** other way in which a plant uses the sugar produced by photosynthesis.

....

[1]

b) Explain why photosynthesis is important for the majority of life on Earth.

....

....

....

....

[3]

[Total 4 marks]

PRACTICAL

3   *Myriophyllum* is an aquatic plant. A student decided to investigate the effect of light intensity on the rate of photosynthesis in *Myriophyllum*.

The student set up a conical flask containing a solution of sodium hydrogencarbonate next to a lamp. She then took five *Myriophyllum* plants and placed them in the conical flask. Finally, she sealed and attached a gas syringe to the test tube and measured the amount of gas collected from the flask in two hours. She repeated this for four more flasks at different distances from the lamp. Her results are shown in **Figure 1**.

Figure 1

Conical flask	Distance away from light (cm)	Gas collected (cm³)	Rate of gas production (cm³ h⁻¹)
1	0	7.8	3.9
2	10	5.0	2.5
3	20	6.0	3.0
4	30	3.4	1.7
5	40	1.2	X

a) Name the gas collected in the gas syringe.

....

[1]

b) Calculate the rate of gas production in **Conical flask 5**.

X = ... cm³ h⁻¹

[1]

c) i) Using the results in **Figure 1**, describe and explain the effect of the distance from the lamp on the rate of gas production in *Myriophyllum*.

....

....

....

....

[3]

ii) Suggest **one** way in which you could increase your confidence in the answer you gave to part c) i).

....

[1]

d) Explain why it is important that the test tubes are all next to the same lamp.

....

....

[2]

[Total 8 marks]

Section 6 — Plant Structures and Their Functions

Limiting Factors in Photosynthesis

1 The distance of a plant from a light source affects the plant's rate of photosynthesis. *Grade 6-7*

a) Name the mathematical law that governs the relationship
between light intensity and distance from a light source.

....

[1]

b) A plant is 40 cm away from a light source. The plant is moved so that it is 20 cm away from the
same light source. Describe how the intensity of light reaching the plant will change.

....

[1]

c) Describe how carbon dioxide concentration also affects the rate of photosynthesis.

....

....

[2]

[Total 4 marks]

2 **Figure 1** shows how temperature affects
the rate of photosynthesis in a green plant. *Grade 6-7*

Figure 1

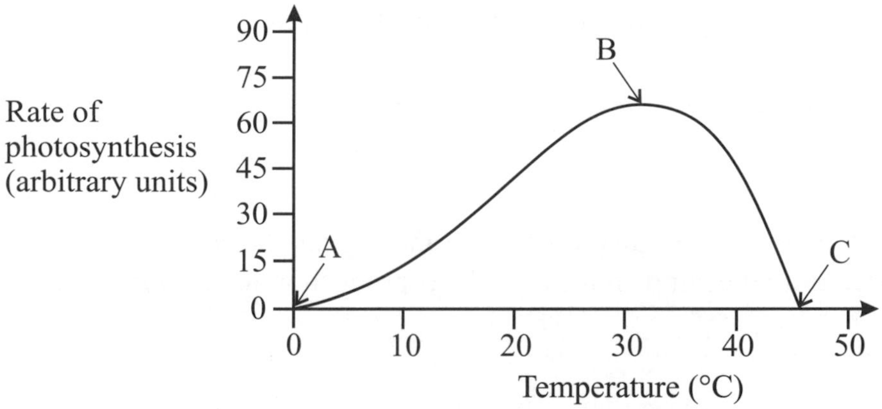

Rate of
photosynthesis
(arbitrary units)

graph: x-axis Temperature (°C) 0 to 50, y-axis 0 to 90. Curve rises from A near origin to peak B around 32°C at ~67, then falls to C at ~46°C.

a) Describe and explain the shape of the curve in **Figure 1** between points **A** and **B**.

....

....

....

[2]

b) Describe and explain the shape of the curve between points **B** and **C**.

....

....

....

....

[3]

[Total 5 marks]

Transport in Plants

Warm-Up

The diagrams below show two different types of vessel involved in the transport of substances in plants. Label them using the words on the right.

A. ....

B. ....

C. ....

D. Cell wall strengthened by ....

E. ....

F. ....

xylem tube

dead cells

living cells

end wall with pores

phloem tube

lignin

---

1 Xylem and phloem tubes are important vessels, which run the length of a plant. *Grade 4-6*

a) i) Name **one** molecule transported via the phloem.

....

[1]

ii) Name **two** molecules transported via the xylem.

1. .... 2. ....

[2]

b) Transport via the phloem:

☐ **A** requires energy. ☐ **C** only occurs in the leaves.

☐ **B** is called transpiration. ☐ **D** only moves substances upwards from the roots.

[1]

[Total 4 marks]

2 *Pythium aphanidermatum* is a pathogen that can infect the roots of a plant, leading to the destruction of many of the root hair cells. *Grade 7-9*

a) Explain how *Pythium* infection may disrupt the transpiration stream.

....

....

....

[2]

b) Why might plants infected with *Pythium* show signs of nutrient deficiency?

....

....

....

[2]

[Total 4 marks]

Section 6 — Plant Structures and Their Functions

Stomata and Transpiration

1   Stomata are mostly found on the lower surface of leaves.   (Grade 4-6)

a)   State the main function of the stomata.

....
[1]

b)   Name the cells which control the size of the stomata.

....
[1]

c)   Explain how the stomata can affect the movement of water up the plant by transpiration.

....

....

....

....
[3]

[Total 5 marks]

2   A group of students were investigating the effect of air flow on the rate of transpiration. They set up their apparatus as shown in **Figure 1**.   (Grade 6-7)

Figure 1

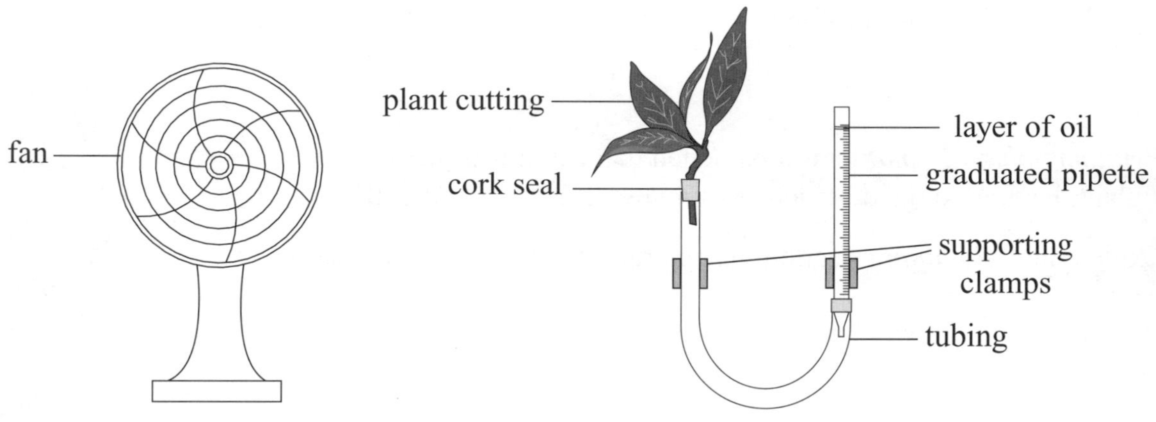

a)   The tubing and graduated pipette were filled with water.
Suggest why a layer of oil was added to the surface of the water in the pipette.

....
[1]

The students recorded the change in the volume of water in the pipette over 30 minutes, in normal conditions. They repeated this five times. They then carried out these steps with the fan turned on to simulate windy conditions. **Figure 2** on the next page shows their results.

Section 6 — Plant Structures and Their Functions

Figure 2

	Repeat	1	2	3	4	5	Mean
Water uptake in 30 minutes (cm³)	Still Air	1.2	1.2	1.0	0.8	1.1	1.1
	Moving Air	2.0	1.8	2.3	1.9	1.7	1.9

b) Draw a bar chart to show the mean water uptake for still air and moving air.

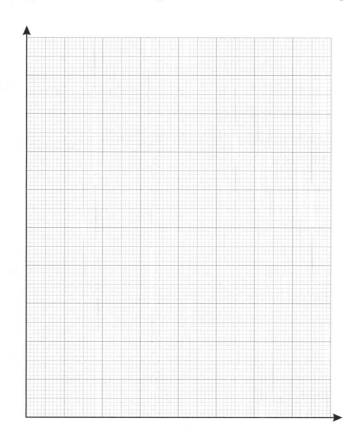

[2]

c) Describe the relationship between air flow around the plant and transpiration rate.

....

[1]

d) Explain the effect of air flow on the rate of transpiration.

....

....

....

[2]

e) Assuming that the mean rate of water uptake is equal to the mean rate of transpiration, calculate the rate of transpiration for the plant in moving air. Give your answer in cm³ hour⁻¹.

.... cm³ hour⁻¹

[2]

[Total 8 marks]

Section 6 — Plant Structures and Their Functions

Hormones

1   The endocrine system is a collection of glands in the body that secrete hormones.   (Grade 4-6)

a) Endocrine glands secrete hormones directly into

☐ **A** cells   ☐ **B** tissues   ☐ **C** blood   ☐ **D** organs

[1]

b) Hormones are

☐ **A** tissues   ☐ **B** cells   ☐ **C** chemicals   ☐ **D** enzymes

[1]

c) **Figure 1** shows the positions of some glands in the human body. Name glands A to E in **Figure 1**.

Figure 1

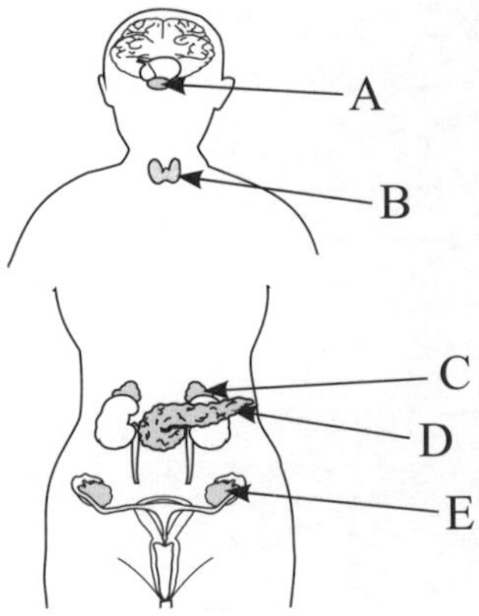

A ....

B ....

C ....

D ....

E ....

[5]

d) State **two** ways in which communication via the endocrine system differs from communication via the nervous system.

1. ....

2. ....

[2]

[Total 9 marks]

2   Males produce a greater amount of testosterone than females. One of the consequences of this, is that males' bones are more dense than females' bones.   (Grade 6-7)

a) Based on the information above, name **one** of testosterone's target organs.

....

[1]

b) A possible treatment for prostate cancer is to have the testes removed. Explain why men who have had their testes removed are more at risk of developing brittle bones.

....

....

....

[2]

[Total 3 marks]

Adrenaline and Thyroxine

Warm-Up

The graph below shows the change in the level of a hormone controlled by a negative feedback response over time.
Use the words on the right to fill in the labels on the graph.

normal   increase in   stimulated

inhibited   decrease in

.... level of hormone detected

release of hormone ....

.... level of hormone

.... level of hormone detected

release of hormone ....

Blood hormone level

Time

1   The hormone adrenaline is produced in times of fear or stress.   *Grade 4-6*

a) Name the glands that release adrenaline.

....

[1]

b) Give **one** effect that adrenaline has on the body.

....

[1]

c) Name the response that adrenaline prepares the body for.

....

[1]

[Total 3 marks]

2   Thyroxine is a hormone.   *Grade 6-7*

a) State **one** role of thyroxine in the body.

....

[1]

b) Explain how the body prevents the level of thyroxine in the blood from getting too high.

....

....

....

....

[3]

[Total 4 marks]

Section 7 — Animal Coordination, Control and Homeostasis

The Menstrual Cycle

1 Oestrogen is a hormone involved in the menstrual cycle. [Grade 4-6]

a) Name the gland that releases oestrogen.

....

[1]

b) Name the hormone that stimulates oestrogen production.

....

[1]

c) Describe how oestrogen effects the uterus lining.

....

[1]

[Total 3 marks]

2 **Figure 1** shows how levels of four different hormones change during the menstrual cycle. [Grade 6-7]

Figure 1

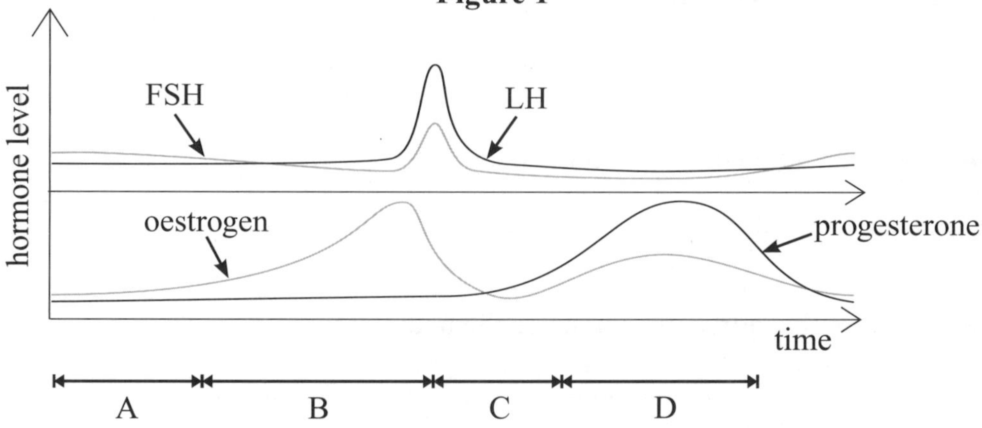

a) During which time period marked on **Figure 1** does menstruation occur?

☐ **A**   ☐ **B**   ☐ **C**   ☐ **D**

[1]

b) Add an arrow (↑) to the *x*-axis on **Figure 1**, to show the time at which ovulation occurs.

[1]

c) Before ovulation can occur, a follicle must mature. Name the hormone that causes this.

....

[1]

d) Explain how the uterus lining is maintained in the days after ovulation.

....

....

....

[3]

[Total 6 marks]

Section 7 — Animal Coordination, Control and Homeostasis

Controlling Fertility

1 Many people choose barrier methods of contraception to prevent pregnancy. *(Grade 4-6)*

a) Give **one** example of a barrier method of contraception.

....

[1]

b) Describe how barrier methods of contraception work.

....

[1]

c) Give **two** advantages of barrier methods of contraception over hormonal methods of contraception.

1. ....

2. ....

[2]

[Total 4 marks]

2 Polycystic ovarian syndrome (PCOS) is a common cause of infertility in women. Women with the disorder don't ovulate regularly. *(Grade 6-7)*

a) Explain why a woman with PCOS may find it hard to get pregnant.

....

....

....

[1]

b) Explain how clomifene therapy could help a woman with PCOS become pregnant.

....

....

....

[3]

c) If clomifene therapy doesn't help the woman to become pregnant, multiple eggs could be collected from the woman's ovaries and then fertilised using the man's sperm. One or two of the resulting embryos could then be transferred to the woman's uterus.

i) State the name given to this process.

....

[1]

ii) Explain why hormones are given to the woman at the beginning of this process.

....

[1]

[Total 6 marks]

Section 7 — Animal Coordination, Control and Homeostasis

3 Some methods of hormonal contraception use oestrogen to help prevent pregnancy. Grade 6-7

a) Explain how oestrogen in hormonal contraceptives helps to prevent pregnancy.

....

....

[2]

b) Many people prefer to use hormonal methods of contraception rather than barrier methods.
Give **two** advantages of hormonal methods of contraception over barrier methods of contraception.

1. ....

2. ....

[2]

[Total 4 marks]

4 The mini pill is a method of oral contraception. It contains progesterone and needs to be taken around the same time every day. Grade 6-7

a) Many women who take the mini pill don't ovulate.

i) Explain how taking the mini pill may prevent ovulation.

....

....

....

[3]

ii) It's not only the effect on ovulation that makes the mini pill an effective contraceptive.
Explain **one** other way in which the mini pill can prevent pregnancy.

....

....

[2]

b) Although the mini pill is an effective method of contraceptive, a couple may still be advised to
use a condom during intercourse. Suggest why.

....

[1]

c) The contraceptive implant is a small tube, which is inserted beneath the skin of the arm and
continuously releases progesterone. It is effective for three years. Suggest **one** reason why a
woman may choose to have a contraceptive implant rather than using the mini pill.

....

[1]

[Total 7 marks]

Exam Practice Tip
Knowing the roles of the hormones that control the menstrual cycle is really important when it comes to understanding how these hormones are used to control fertility. So make sure you've got it all sorted out in your head.

Section 7 — Animal Coordination, Control and Homeostasis

Homeostasis — Control of Blood Glucose

1 Homeostasis involves the regulation of blood glucose concentration. Grade 4-6

a) Explain what is meant by the term 'homeostasis'.

....

[1]

b) Name the gland in the body that monitors and controls blood glucose concentration.

....

[1]

[Total 2 marks]

2 In an experiment, the blood glucose concentration of a person was recorded at regular intervals in a 90 minute time period. Fifteen minutes into the experiment, a glucose drink was given. **Figure 1** shows the results of the experiment. Grade 7-9

Figure 1

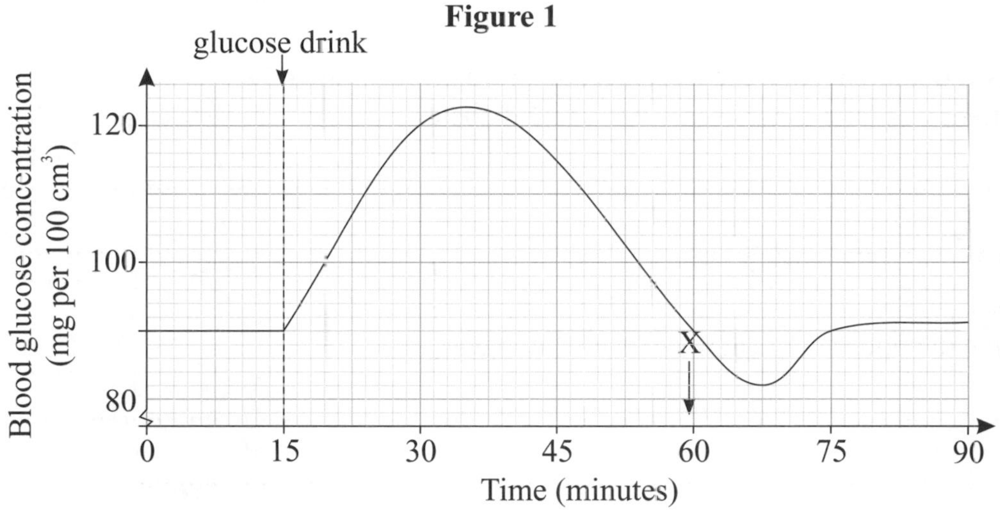

a) Explain what is happening to the blood glucose concentration between 15 and 60 minutes.

....

....

....

[3]

b) i) Name the hormone being released by the pancreas at point **X** on the graph.

....

[1]

ii) Explain how the hormone released at point **X** affects the blood glucose concentration.

....

....

....

[3]

[Total 7 marks]

    Section 7 — Animal Coordination, Control and Homeostasis

Diabetes

1   A patient visits her health centre because she is concerned she is at risk of developing type 2 diabetes.   **Grade 6-7**

   a) i) Firstly, a nurse measures the patient's mass and height. Explain why he does this.

....

....

                                                                                             [2]

     ii) Next the nurse uses his tape measure to take **two** other measurements of the patient's body. Suggest which two measurements he takes. Explain your answer.

....

....

....

                                                                                             [3]

   b) Give **two** treatments that the patient's doctor might recommend if the patient was later diagnosed with type 2 diabetes.

     1. ....

     2. ....

                                                                                              [2]

   c) Describe the underlying causes of type 2 diabetes.

....

....

                                                                                              [2]

                                                                   [Total 9 marks]

2   In rare cases, type 1 diabetes may be treated with a pancreas transplant.   **Grade 7-9**

   a) i) Explain why a pancreas transplant could be used to treat a person with type 1 diabetes.

....

....

                                                                                                [2]

     ii) Suggest **one** reason why a pancreas transplant is rarely used to treat type 1 diabetes.

....

....

                                                                                                [1]

   b) State the main form of treatment for type 1 diabetes.

....

                                                                                                [1]

                                                                        [Total 5 marks]

Section 7 — Animal Coordination, Control and Homeostasis

Exchange of Materials

Warm-Up

Complete the calculations below to work out the surface area and volume of the shape on the right.

Surface area: (8 mm × .... mm) × 2
+ (8 mm × .... mm) × 4
= .... mm²

Volume: .... mm × .... mm × .... mm
= .... mm³

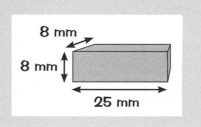

8 mm
8 mm
25 mm

---

1   In order to survive, mammals, like all organisms, must exchange substances with their environment.

Grade 4-6

a) Give **two** substances that a mammal must transport into its body in order to survive.

....

[2]

b) Give **two** substances that a mammal must get rid of in order to survive.

....

[2]

[Total 4 marks]

---

2   A student was investigating the effect of size on the uptake of substances by diffusion. He cut different sized cubes of agar containing universal indicator and placed them in beakers of acid. He timed how long it took for the acid to diffuse through to the centre of each cube (and so change the colour of the agar).

Grade 7-9

Figure 1 shows the relationship between the surface area and volume of the agar cubes.

Figure 1

a) Calculate the values of X, Y and Z in **Figure 1**.

Cube size (cm)	Surface area (cm²)	Volume (cm³)	Simple ratio
2 × 2 × 2	24	8	3:1
3 × 3 × 3	**X**	**Y**	2:1
5 × 5 × 5	150	125	**Z** : 1

X = ... cm²

Y = ... cm³

Z = ...

[3]

b) Explain which cube would take the longest to change colour.

....

....

[1]

[Total 4 marks]

Specialised Exchange Surfaces — the Alveoli

1 Sticklebacks are a type of freshwater fish. They have specialised
exchange surfaces, called gills, and a mass transport system powered
by a heart. Explain why a stickleback needs both specialised
exchange surfaces and a mass transport system in order to survive.

Grade 6-7

....

....

....

....

....

....

[Total 4 marks]

2 **Figure 3** shows an alveolus in the lungs. *Grade 6-7*

Figure 3

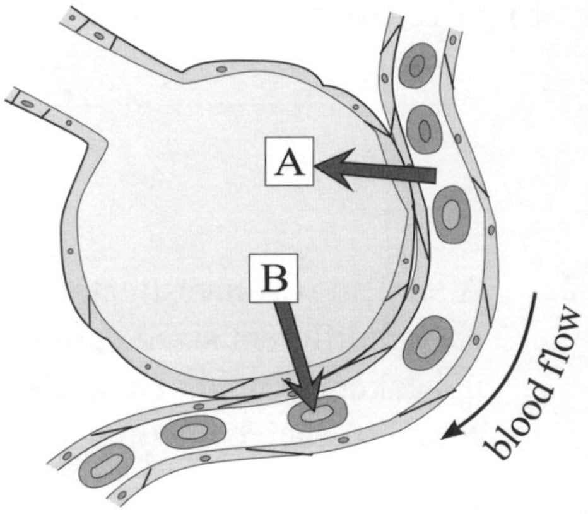

a) Name the gases A and B.

A ....

B ....

[2]

b) Gases A and B move down their concentration gradients
by diffusion. Explain how the blood flow at an alveolus
ensures there is a high rate of diffusion for both gases
following the inhalation of air.

....

....

....

....

....

[3]

c) Other than a good blood supply, explain **two** ways in which alveoli in the lungs are adapted
for gas exchange.

1. ....

....

2. ....

....

[4]

[Total 9 marks]

Section 8 — Exchange and Transport in Animals

Circulatory System — Blood

1 The blood is composed of different components, each of which has a different function. **Grade 4-6**

a) Which of the following are types of white blood cell?

☐ **A** phagoctytes and lysozymes ☐ **C** phagoctytes and erythrocytes

☐ **B** phagoctytes and lymphocytes ☐ **D** erythrocytes and lymphocytes

[1]

b) Name the component of the blood that produces antibodies.

....

[1]

c) Describe the structure and function of blood plasma.

....

....

[2]

[Total 4 marks]

2 The components of blood can be separated by spinning them at high speed. **Figure 1** shows a tube of blood that has been separated in this way. **Grade 6-7**

Figure 1

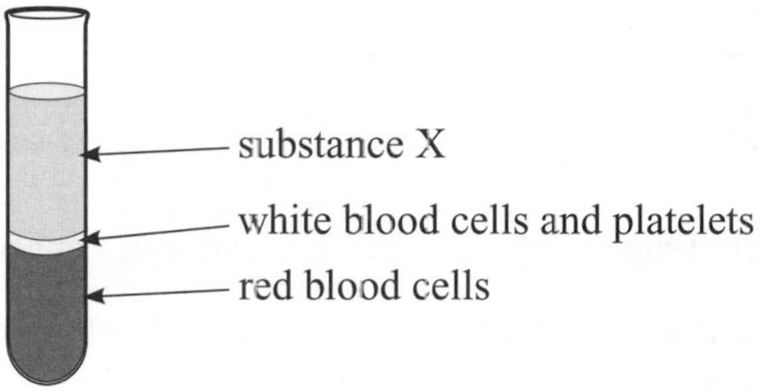

substance X

white blood cells and platelets

red blood cells

a) Identify the substance labelled X in **Figure 1**.

....

[1]

b) Red blood cells have a biconcave shape. Explain how this allows them to fulfil their function.

....

....

[2]

c) A scientist analysing the blood sample found that it had a lower than normal concentration of platelets. Explain one problem the patient may experience due to this.

....

....

....

[2]

[Total 5 marks]

Section 8 — Exchange and Transport in Animals

Circulatory System — Blood Vessels

Label each of the following diagrams to indicate whether they represent a capillary, artery or vein.

Diagrams not to scale.

A. ....Artery............   B. ....vein...........   C. ......capillary........

---

1 Blood vessels can be identified by their structure or location in the body. (Grade 4-6)

a) i) Name the type of blood vessel that has valves.

....
[1]

ii) Describe the purpose of valves in a blood vessel.

....
[1]

b) Name the type of blood vessel that joins up to form veins.

....
[1]

[Total 3 marks]

---

2 Different types of blood vessel perform different functions. (Grade 6-7)

a) Veins and arteries both have a layer of smooth muscle within their walls. Which of these types of blood vessel has a thicker layer of muscle? Explain your answer with reference to their functions.

....

....

....

....
[4]

b) Capillaries are very narrow. Explain how this allows them to fulfil their function.

....

....
[2]

[Total 6 marks]

> ### *Exam Practice Tip*
> There are lots of places in this topic where you could be asked how the structure of something is related to its function. In these sorts of questions, don't just describe the function then rattle off what it looks like — make sure you clearly explain how each structural feature you mention helps with the function.

Circulatory System — Heart

Complete the following passage by circling the correct bold word or phrase in each sentence.

Deoxygenated / oxygenated blood enters the right atrium through the **vena cava / aorta**.

From there it is pumped into the **right ventricle / pulmonary vein**. Then it is pumped

up through the pulmonary **vein / artery** towards the **lungs / rest of the body**.

A **valve / low pressure** prevents the blood from flowing back into the right atrium.

1   The heart pumps blood around the body. **Figure 1** shows a diagram of the heart.

Figure 1

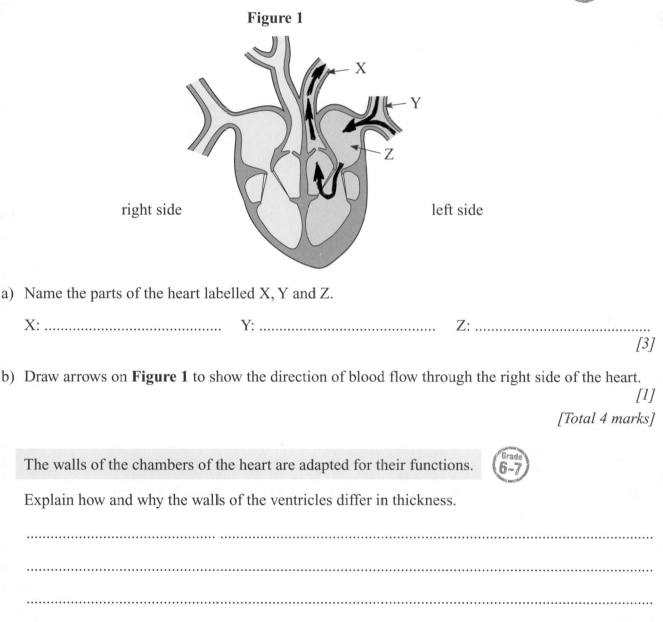

right side   left side

a) Name the parts of the heart labelled X, Y and Z.

X: ....   Y: ....   Z: ....
[3]

b) Draw arrows on **Figure 1** to show the direction of blood flow through the right side of the heart.
[1]
[Total 4 marks]

2   The walls of the chambers of the heart are adapted for their functions.

Explain how and why the walls of the ventricles differ in thickness.

....

....

....

....

....
[Total 3 marks]

Section 8 — Exchange and Transport in Animals

3   A scientist was investigating the effect of height on cardiac output in athletes. He predicted that taller athletes would have a greater cardiac output than shorter athletes, as taller athletes are likely to have larger hearts. Before he measured their heights, the scientist measured the stroke volume and resting heart rate of each athlete, and calculated their cardiac output. His results for two of the athletes are shown in **Figure 2**.

Figure 2

Athlete	1	2
Heart rate (bpm)	57	**Y**
Stroke volume (cm³)	84	65
Cardiac output (cm³ min⁻¹)	**X**	4095

a) Explain what is meant by the term 'stroke volume'.

....

....

[1]

b) Calculate the cardiac output for Athlete **1**.

Cardiac output = ... cm³ min⁻¹

[2]

c) Calculate the heart rate for Athlete **2**.

Heart rate = ... bpm

[2]

d) Suggest an explanation as to why the scientist predicted that a larger heart would result in a greater cardiac output.

....

....

....

....

....

[3]

e) The scientist asks the athletes to cycle for 10 minutes to increase their heart rate. Explain how exercise will affect the athletes' cardiac output.

....

[1]

[Total 9 marks]

Exam Practice Tip

The structure of the heart and the way blood flows through it can be pretty tricky to get your head around. In the exam you might find it helpful to sketch a quick diagram of the heart and the way blood flows through it to help you answer questions on it. Make sure you really know how to calculate heart rate, stroke volume and cardiac output too.

Respiration

1 Respiration is an exothermic reaction. It can occur either aerobically or anaerobically. [Grade 6-7]

a) What does it mean if a reaction is exothermic?

☐ **A** It releases energy to the environment.

☐ **B** It produces carbon dioxide.

☐ **C** It takes in energy from the environment.

☐ **D** It is used in metabolism.

[1]

b) Explain why respiration reactions are essential for the life of an organism.

....

....

[2]

c) i) Name a substance that is broken down in both aerobic and anaerobic respiration.

....

[1]

ii) Name a substance that is broken down in aerobic respiration but not in anaerobic respiration.

....

[1]

iii) Name the products of aerobic respiration.

....

[2]

d) Give **one** reason why it may be more beneficial for the body to use aerobic respiration to transfer energy most of the time, rather than using anaerobic respiration.

....

....

[1]

e) Give **one** example of a situation in which a person may begin to respire anaerobically.

....

[1]

f) Describe how the products of anaerobic respiration differ between plants and animals.

....

....

....

[3]

[Total 12 marks]

Section 8 — Exchange and Transport in Animals

2 The air that a person inhales has a different composition from the air that they exhale. **Figure 1** shows the percentages of different gases in the inhaled air and in the exhaled air.

a) Explain the difference in the values for the percentage of oxygen in inhaled and exhaled air.

....

....

....

....

[1]

Figure 1

	Inhaled air (%)	Exhaled air (%)
Nitrogen	78	78
Oxygen	21	16
Carbon dioxide		
Other gases	0.9	0.9

b) Explain how the percentage of carbon dioxide would differ between inhaled and exhaled air.

....

....

[2]

[Total 3 marks]

3 A scientist was measuring the effects of exercise on respiration. He asked a male volunteer to jog for 10 minutes on a treadmill. The speed of the treadmill was increased over the course of the 10 minutes, so that he was gradually working harder, until at the end he felt unable to do any more exercise. **Figure 2** shows the oxygen consumption (the amount of oxygen used by the body per minute) of the man during the exercise.

Figure 2

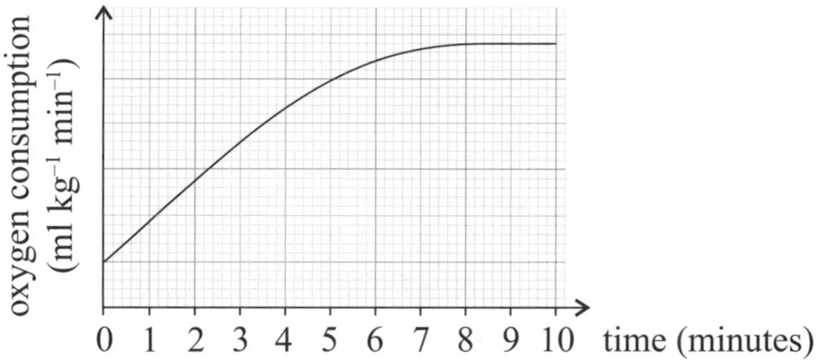

a) Describe how oxygen consumption changed during the exercise.

....

....

[2]

b) In the final two minutes of the exercise, the man was respiring anaerobically. Explain how the scientist may know this by looking at the graph in **Figure 2**.

....

....

....

....

[2]

[Total 4 marks]

Investigating Respiration

1   An experiment was set up using two sealed beakers, each with a
carbon dioxide monitor attached. The set up is shown in **Figure 1**.

Figure 1

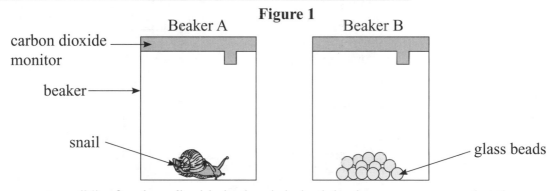

The percentage (%) of carbon dioxide in the air in both beakers was measured at the
start of the experiment and again after 2 hours. The results are shown in **Figure 2**.

Figure 2

Time	% carbon dioxide in the air	
(hours)	Beaker A	Beaker B
0	0.04	0.04
2	0.10	0.04

a) Suggest **one** ethical consideration that must be taken into account during this experiment.

....

[1]

b) Explain the purpose of the glass beads in Beaker B.

....

....

[2]

c) Explain the results for Beaker A.

....

....

[1]

d) Explain how the level of oxygen in Beaker A would have changed during the experiment.

....

....

[2]

e) Suggest how the internal temperature of Beaker A would differ from that of Beaker B
during the experiment. Explain your answer.

....

....

....

[2]

[Total 8 marks]

Ecosystems & Interactions Between Organisms

Warm-Up

Put the words below into the correct column in the table, according to whether they are abiotic or biotic factors in an organism's environment.

Abiotic	Biotic

pollutants   light intensity   water

temperature   prey species

competition   predators

---

1   There are different levels of organisation within a habitat.   *(Grade 4-6)*

a)   A community is

☐   **A**   all the organisms of one species living in a habitat.

☐   **B**   all the organisms of different species living in a habitat.

☐   **C**   all the organisms of one population living in a habitat.

☐   **D**   all of the abiotic and biotic factors in an habitat.

[1]

b)   Explain what is meant by the term 'ecosystem'.

....

[1]

[Total 2 marks]

---

2   Grasses make their own food by photosynthesis. In grassland communities, the grass leaves provide insects with shelter, a place to breed and a source of food. Visiting birds feed on insects.   *(Grade 6-7)*

a)   Explain what you would expect to happen to the birds visiting the grassland if a new insect predator entered the ecosystem.

....

....

[2]

b)   The number of birds visiting the grassland decreases. What would you eventually expect to happen to the number of grass plants? Explain your answer.

....

....

....

[3]

[Total 5 marks]

3 A cuckoo is a type of bird that lays its eggs in the nest of another bird. When the cuckoo egg hatches, the cuckoo chick kills some of the offspring of the host and the host bird raises the cuckoo chick as if it was its own.

Grade 6-7

a) Name the type of interaction between a cuckoo chick and its host. Explain your answer.

....

....

[2]

b) Ants often live in the hollow thorns on a certain species of tree. The ants living in the trees feed on the trees' nectar. When herbivores try to graze on the trees, the ants bite them. Some ant species have also been shown to protect the trees from harmful bacteria.

Which of the following statements best describes the relationship between the ants and the trees?

☐ **A** The ants are parasites because they depend entirely on the trees to survive.

☐ **B** The relationship is mutualistic because both the ants and the trees benefit from it.

☐ **C** The relationship is parasitic because the host is harmed and doesn't benefit from it.

☐ **D** The relationship is mutualistic because the trees depend on the ants to survive.

[1]

[Total 3 marks]

4 Prickly acacia is a tree species native to Africa, and parts of Asia. It was introduced to Australia many years ago. It has invaded large areas of land in the warmer parts of the country. The trees grow best in areas with a high average temperature and where there is plenty of water, such as along rivers or on flood plains where there is seasonal flooding.

Grade 6-7

a) Australia experienced particularly high rainfall in the 1950s and 1970s.
Explain how the prickly acacia population in Australia may have changed during these periods.

....

....

[2]

b) Global temperature is thought to be increasing. What may happen to the distribution of prickly acacia in Australia over the next few decades? Explain your answer.

....

....

....

[2]

c) When prickly acacia invade an area it can negatively impact the populations of various grasses in that area. Explain why this might be the case.

....

....

[2]

[Total 6 marks]

Section 9 — Ecosystems and Material Cycles

Investigating Ecosystems

1   A group of students used a 0.5 m² quadrat to investigate the number of buttercups growing in a field. They counted the number of buttercups in the quadrat in ten randomly selected places. **Figure 1** shows their results.

Figure 1

Quadrat Number	Number of buttercups
1	15
2	13
3	16
4	23
5	26
6	23
7	13
8	12
9	16
10	13

a) i) Explain why it is important that the quadrats were randomly placed in the field.

....
[1]

ii) Describe a method that could have been used to randomly place the quadrats.

....
[1]

b) What is the modal number of buttercups in a quadrat in **Figure 1**?

.... buttercups
[1]

c) What is the median number of buttercups in **Figure 1**?

.... buttercups
[1]

d) Calculate the mean number of buttercups per 0.5 m² quadrat.

.... buttercups per 0.5 m²
[1]

e) The total area of the field was 1750 m².
Estimate the number of buttercups in the whole of the field.

.... buttercups
[2]
[Total 7 marks]

2 A belt transect was carried out from the edge of a small pond, across a grassy field and into a woodland. The distributions of four species of plant were recorded along the transect, along with the soil moisture and light levels. **Figure 2** shows the results.

Grade 6-7

Figure 2

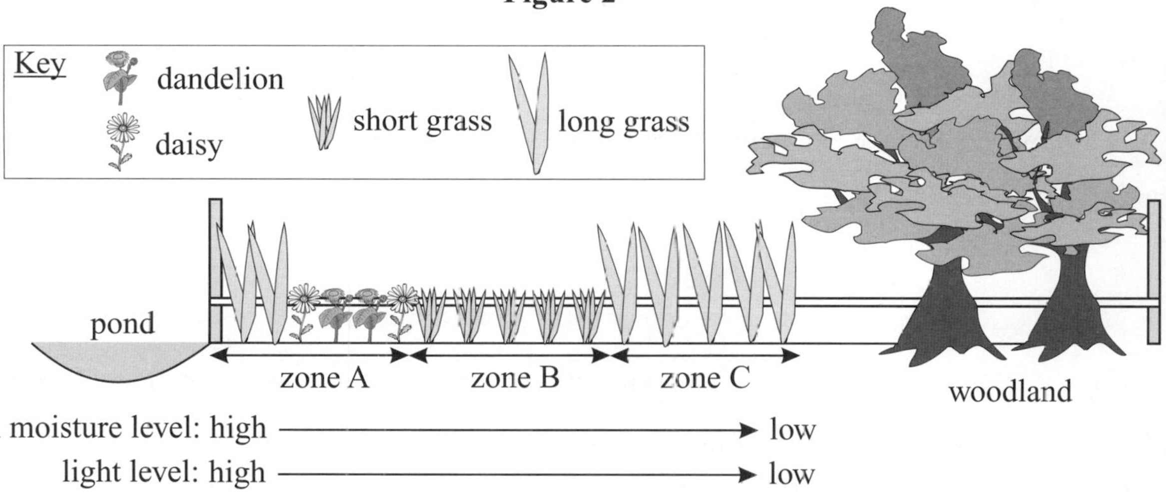

Key
dandelion
daisy
short grass   long grass

pond   zone A   zone B   zone C   woodland

soil moisture level: high ⟶ low
light level: high ⟶ low

The grassy field is split up into three zones — A, B and C.

a) In **Figure 2**, which zones of the grassy field contained only one species of plant?

....

[1]

b) Which of the four species of plant can grow in soils with both a high and low moisture level, and at both low and high light intensities?

....

[1]

c) Suggest **two** reasons why daisies and dandelions can grow in zone A.

1. ....

2. ....

[2]

Children often play football on one zone of the grassy field.
The trampling that occurs here makes it difficult for plants to become established.

d) Suggest which zone might be used to play football. Explain your answer.

....

....

[2]

e) Suggest why none of the plants growing in zones A to C were found in the woodland.

....

[1]

[Total 7 marks]

> **Exam Practice Tip**
> Be careful with any calculations you're asked to make — the maths on the previous page isn't hard, but you need to make sure you don't mix up the mean, mode and median.

Human Impacts on Biodiversity

1 Possums are a type of marsupial mammal native to Australia. In the 1800s they were introduced by humans into New Zealand for the fur trade.

Grade 6-7

Suggest **two** reasons why possums may have negatively affected species native to New Zealand.

1. ....

   ....

2. ....

   ....

[Total 2 marks]

2 Human interactions with ecosystems can change the abiotic conditions, reducing biodiversity.

a)* Explain how the application of fertilisers on farmland may reduce the biodiversity of nearby water sources.

Grade 7-9

....

....

....

....

....

....

....

....

....

[6]

b) Fish can be farmed in nets in the ocean. However, this method of fish farming can cause similar problems to excess fertilisers in surrounding waters. Suggest an explanation for this.

....

....

[2]

c) Explain **two** other potential impacts of open water fish farms on the biodiversity of their surrounding environment.

1. ....

   ....

2. ....

   ....

[2]

[Total 10 marks]

Section 9 — Ecosystems and Material Cycles

Conservation and Biodiversity

1 Conservation efforts often aim to protect a single endangered species, e.g. the panda. Grade 6-7

a) Explain **one** reason why efforts to protect one species may help to protect many others as well.

....

....

....

[2]

b) Suggest **one** reason why the protection of a species may benefit the economy of a country.

....

....

[1]

[Total 3 marks]

2* Human activity has reduced the forest cover in Ethiopia significantly. Land that used to be covered by trees is now more exposed to rainfall in the rainy season, leading to increased soil loss through erosion, and heat from the Sun during the dry season, leading to drought. Reforestation programmes employ local people to plant trees over large areas of land. Grade 7-9

Discuss why reforestation may be beneficial for Ethiopia. Include details about the potential benefits for biodiversity, local farmers and Ethiopian society.

....

....

....

....

....

....

....

....

....

....

....

[Total 6 marks]

The Carbon Cycle

1   **Figure 1** shows an unfinished diagram of the carbon cycle.

Figure 1

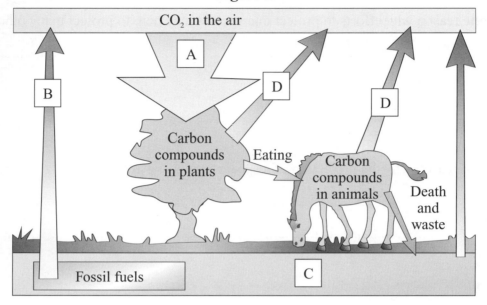

a) i) Name the process represented by **A** in **Figure 1**.

....

[1]

ii) Describe the importance of process **A** for an ecosystem.

....

....

[1]

b) Name the process represented by **B** in **Figure 1**.

....

[1]

c) Process **C** in **Figure 1** is decay. Describe the importance of decay in the carbon cycle.

....

....

[2]

d) Give **one** biotic and **one** abiotic component of the ecosystem represented in **Figure 1**.

Biotic: ....

Abiotic: ....

[2]

[Total 7 marks]

Exam Practice Tip

In the exam you could be tested on any part of the carbon cycle, so make sure you know the whole of it and not just bits of it. Try sketching the whole cycle out and make sure you can link each bit together. Don't have your arrows going the wrong way round, and make sure you understand why the carbon is moving around, e.g. because of respiration. Sorted.

     ☐   ☐   ☐

The Water Cycle

Choose from the words below to complete the sentences about the water cycle. Some words may not be used at all.

precipitation   evaporate   warms   cools   water vapour   carbon dioxide   condense

Energy from the Sun makes water .... from the land and sea,

turning it into .... This is carried upwards. When it gets higher

up it .... and condenses to form clouds. Water falls from the

clouds as .... onto land. It then drains into the sea, before the

whole process starts again.

1 The water cycle is important in recycling water so that it is available for use by organisms. *(Grade 4-6)*

a) Potable water is:

☐ **A** sea water.

☐ **B** drinking water.

☐ **C** contaminated water.

☐ **D** evaporated water.

[1]

b) Explain why sea water is not suitable for drinking by humans.

....

[1]

[Total 2 marks]

2 Somalia is a country on the eastern coast of Africa. In 2011, a lack of rainfall in Somalia led to a severe drought. *(Grade 7-9)*

Describe and explain **one** method of desalination which may have been used in Somalia to provide water suitable for drinking.

....

....

....

....

....

....

[Total 4 marks]

Section 9 — Ecosystems and Material Cycles

The Nitrogen Cycle

1 Nitrogen makes up roughly 78% of the gases in the atmosphere. Carbon dioxide makes up only 0.04%. Plants need to absorb both gases in order to survive and grow.

a) Give **one** reason why plants need nitrogen in order to grow.

....

[1]

b) Plants absorb carbon dioxide from the air. Which of the following sentences (**A-D**) describes why plants must rely on microorganisms in order to absorb nitrogen?

☐ **A** The nitrogen in the atmosphere is too dense.

☐ **B** The nitrogen in the atmosphere is too unreactive.

☐ **C** Plants only need nitrogen in their roots.

☐ **D** The nitrogen in the atmosphere is too far away from the plants' leaves.

[1]

[Total 2 marks]

2 **Figure 1** shows a simplified diagram of the nitrogen cycle.

Figure 1

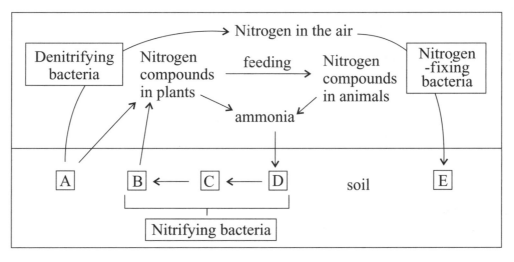

a) All of the letters on **Figure 1** represent a type of mineral ion.
List **all** of the letters on **Figure 1** which represent:

i) nitrites

....

ii) ammonium ions

....

iii) nitrates

....

[5]

b) Lightning can cause a reaction between nitrogen and oxygen in the air to produce nitrates.
What type of reaction is this?

☐ **A** nitrification ☐ **B** denitrification ☐ **C** decomposition ☐ **D** nitrogen fixation

[1]

c) Describe the role of decomposers in the nitrogen cycle.

....

....

[2]

[Total 8 marks]

3   Yellow leaves are a common symptom of nitrogen deficiency in plants. A gardener noticed
that some of his cabbages were showing yellow leaves. He then decided to replant his
cabbages in a plot in which he had previously grown pea plants. Peas are a type of legume.
After replanting, the cabbages' growth improved and their leaves became less yellow.

(Grade 7-9)

a) Explain why the cabbages' leaves became less yellow after replanting.

....

....

....

....

[3]

b) The gardener decided to use the original cabbage plot to plant other vegetables. Explain why it
might be a good idea for him to spread manure or compost on the plot before planting anything.

....

....

[1]

c) Denitrifying bacteria are most active in anaerobic conditions, such as in waterlogged soils.
Explain **one** reason why the cabbages may show yellow leaves again after a particularly
wet season.

....

....

....

....

[3]

[Total 7 marks]

Exam Practice Tip

The nitrogen cycle is a bit more complicated than either the water cycle or the carbon cycle, and a lot of the names for
the different processes sound really quite similar. Before you do anything else, make sure you get the differences between
nitrification, nitrogen fixation, decomposition and denitrification sorted in your head. Drawing out the cycle always helps.

Section 10 — Key Concepts in Chemistry

Chemical Equations

1 Hydrogen gas is used as a reactant in the Haber Process. It can be made using the following reaction.

$$CH_4 + H_2O \rightarrow CO + 3H_2$$

Which of the following word equations correctly describes this reaction? Tick **one** box.

☐ **A** methane + water → carbon dioxide + hydrogen

☐ **B** ethane + water → carbon dioxide + hydrogen

☐ **C** methane + water → carbon monoxide + hydrogen

☐ **D** methane + water → carbon + oxygen + hydrogen

[Total 1 mark]

2 Calcium carbonate chips were reacted with nitric acid at room temperature. The products of the reaction were water, a gas and a salt solution.

Complete the reaction equation by adding state symbols to describe the reaction.

$$CaCO_3(..........) + 2HNO_3(..........) \rightarrow Ca(NO_3)_2(..........) + H_2O(..........) + CO_2(..........)$$

[Total 2 marks]

3 Sodium metal can react with oxygen molecules in the air to form sodium oxide (Na_2O).

Write a balanced equation for this reaction.

....

[Total 2 marks]

4 In a chemical reaction, sulfuric acid and aluminium metal react to form hydrogen gas and a salt solution of aluminium sulfate.

Ben has written this equation for the reaction:

$$Al_{(s)} + H_2SO_{4\,(aq)} \rightarrow Al_2(SO_4)_{3\,(aq)} + H_{2\,(g)}$$

a) Explain what is meant by the symbol '(aq)' in the chemical equation.

....

[1]

b) Ben's equation is not balanced. Write a balanced chemical equation for this reaction.

....

[1]

[Total 2 marks]

5 Nitric acid can be made using ammonia.

a) The first stage in the manufacture of nitric acid is to oxidise ammonia, NH_3, to nitrogen(II) oxide, NO. Balance the equation for the reaction.

$$\text{.........} NH_3 + \text{.........} O_2 \rightarrow \text{.........} NO + \text{.........} H_2O$$

[1]

b) The reaction below shows the final stage in the manufacture of nitric acid. The equation is not balanced correctly. Explain how you can tell.

$$2NO_2 + O_2 + H_2O \rightarrow 2HNO_3$$

....

....

[1]

[Total 2 marks]

6 Silver chloride, AgCl, can be made by reacting silver nitrate, $AgNO_3$, and sodium chloride, NaCl, together in a precipitation reaction.

$$AgNO_{3\,(aq)} + NaCl_{(aq)} \rightarrow AgCl_{(s)} + NaNO_{3\,(aq)}$$

a) How can you tell from the reaction equation that this is a precipitation reaction?

....

[1]

b) Write a balanced ionic equation for the reaction above.

....

[2]

[Total 3 marks]

7 Balance the following symbol equation to show how sulfur reacts with nitric acid.

$$S + HNO_3 \rightarrow H_2SO_4 + NO_2 + H_2O$$

....

[Total 1 mark]

8 Zinc reacts with tin sulfate solution in a redox reaction. The full reaction equation is shown below.

$$Zn_{(s)} + SnSO_{4\,(aq)} \rightarrow ZnSO_{4\,(aq)} + Sn_{(s)}$$

Write the ionic equation for the reaction above.

....

[Total 2 marks]

Section 10 — Key Concepts in Chemistry

Hazards and Risk

1 Eric is carrying out an experiment using some hazardous chemicals. One of the chemicals is stored in a flask, marked with the label shown in **Figure 1**.

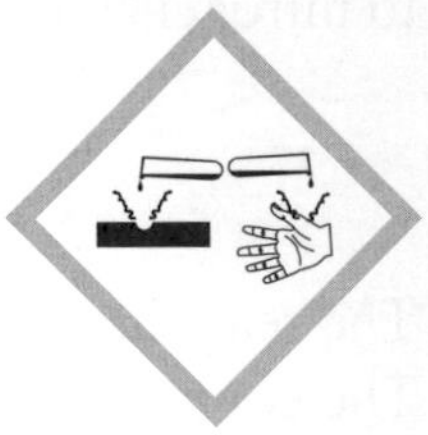

Grade 4-6

Figure 1

a) Which of the following hazards are associated with the contents of the flask? Tick **one** box.

☐ **A** oxidising ☐ **C** harmful

☐ **B** corrosive ☐ **D** highly flammable

[1]

b) Suggest **one** safety precaution that Eric should take when using the chemical from the flask.

....

[1]

[Total 2 marks]

2 A lab technician is cleaning up a lab after an experiment. The experiment involved using chemicals from flasks marked with the label shown in **Figure 2**.

Grade 6-7

With reference to **Figure 2**, explain why the technician needs to be careful when disposing of the chemicals.

Figure 2

....

....

[Total 2 marks]

3* A student is planning an experiment to assess how the rate of a certain reaction changes with concentration. The reaction involves her using chemicals that are marked as harmful and corrosive. It also produces a gas.

Grade 7-9

Construct a risk assessment to outline the hazards associated with the experiment and the safety precautions that the student should take to reduce them.

....

....

....

....

....

....

....

....

[Total 6 marks]

The History of the Atom

Draw **one** line from each atomic model to the correct description of that model.

Atomic Model   **Description**

Plum pudding model

A positively charged 'ball' with negatively charged electrons in it.

A small, positively charged nucleus surrounded by a 'cloud' of negative electrons.

Bohr's model

Electrons in fixed orbits surrounding a small, positively charged nucleus.

Rutherford's nuclear model

Solid spheres with a different sphere for each element.

---

1 Models of the atom have changed over time. (Grade 4-6)

Which of the following statements is the best description of what scientists thought an atom was like before the electron was discovered? Tick **one** box.

☐ **A** Tiny solid spheres that can't be divided.   ☐ **C** Flat geometric shapes.

☐ **B** Formless 'clouds' of matter.   ☐ **D** Discrete packets of energy.

[Total 1 mark]

---

2 In 1911, Rutherford, Geiger and Marsden carried out the gold foil experiment. They fired positively charged alpha particles at gold foil. They predicted that most of the particles would pass straight through the foil and a few might be deflected slightly. (Grade 6-7)

a) Describe what actually happened to the alpha particles during the gold foil experiment and explain why it happened.

....

....

....

....

[4]

b) Name the scientist who adapted Rutherford's nuclear model by suggesting that electrons orbit the nucleus at specific distances.

....

[1]

[Total 5 marks]

Section 10 — Key Concepts in Chemistry

The Atom

1 **Figure 1** shows the structure of a certain atom. Grade 4-6

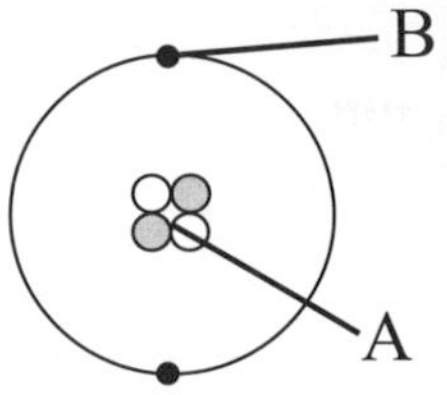

a) Name the region where most of the mass of the atom is concentrated.

.... [1]

b) What is the name of particle **B**?

.... [1]

c) State the **two** subatomic particles which are present in region **A**.

.... [1]

d) Use the relative charges of the subatomic particles to explain why an atom has no overall charge.

....

....

....

.... [3]

e) The atom shown in **Figure 1** has an atomic number of 2.
What is the name of the element that the atom in **Figure 1** makes up? Tick **one** box.

☐ **A** hydrogen ☐ **B** lithium ☐ **C** helium ☐ **D** beryllium

[1]

[Total 7 marks]

Figure 1

2 A potassium atom can be represented by the nuclear symbol $^{39}_{19}K$. Grade 4-6

a) What is the mass number of $^{39}_{19}K$?

.... [1]

b) What is the atomic number of $^{39}_{19}K$?

.... [1]

c) How many protons, neutrons and electrons does an atom of $^{39}_{19}K$ have?

protons: .... neutrons: .... electrons: ....

[3]

[Total 5 marks]

Isotopes and Relative Atomic Mass

1 This question is about isotopes.

a) A neutral atom of sulfur, ^{32}S, has 16 electrons.
Sulfur has three other naturally occurring isotopes, with mass numbers 33, 34 and 36.
Complete the table in **Figure 1**, giving the number of protons, neutrons and
electrons for each of the naturally occurring isotopes of sulfur.

Isotope	Number of Protons	Number of Neutrons	Number of Electrons
^{32}S	....	....	16
^{33}S	....	....	....
^{34}S	....	....	....
^{36}S	....	....	....

Figure 1

[3]

b) Atom **X** has a mass number of 51 and an atomic number of 23.
Atom **Y** has a mass number of 51 and an atomic number of 22.
Atom **Z** has a mass number of 52 and an atomic number of 23.

Identify which pair of atoms are isotopes and explain why.

....

....

....

[3]

[Total 6 marks]

2 **Figure 2** shows some information about three isotopes of silicon.

Name	Atomic Number	Mass Number	Abundance (%)
Silicon-28	14	28	92.2
Silicon-29	14	29	4.70
Silicon-30	14	30	3.10

Figure 2

a) How many neutrons does an atom of silicon-29 contain?

neutrons = ...

[1]

b) Work out the relative atomic mass of silicon.

relative atomic mass = ...

[2]

[Total 3 marks]

3 Bromine has two main isotopes: Br-79 and Br-81. *Grade 6-7*

a) Give the definition of the term **isotopes**.

....

....
[1]

b) Bromine has an atomic number of 35. Calculate the number of neutrons in both isotopes.

Br-79 : .... neutrons

Br-81 : .... neutrons
[1]

c) The relative isotopic abundances of bromine-79 and bromine-81 are 12.67 and 12.32 respectively. Calculate the relative atomic mass of bromine. Give your answer to 2 significant figures.

relative atomic mass = ...
[2]
[Total 4 marks]

4 The relative atomic mass of every element can be found in the periodic table. *Grade 6-7*

a) Give the definition of the **relative atomic mass** of an element.

....

....
[2]

b) Explain why some elements have relative atomic masses that are not whole numbers.

....

....
[1]
[Total 3 marks]

5 Gallium can exist as two stable isotopes: Ga-69 and Ga-71. *Grade 7-9*

Give than 60.1% of gallium atoms are Ga-69 atoms, and the rest are Ga-71 atoms, calculate the relative atomic mass of gallium.

relative atomic mass = ...
[Total 3 marks]

Exam Practice Tip

Don't let isotopes confuse you. Just because they've got different numbers of neutrons, a pair of isotopes will still have the same number of protons, so they're still the same element. Those relative atomic mass calculations aren't too bad either. Remember — if your isotopic abundances are given as percentages, then they should always add up to 100%.

The Periodic Table

1 Chemical elements are arranged in the periodic table. [Grade 4-6]

a) How are the elements ordered in the modern periodic table?

....

[1]

b) Why do elements in groups have similar chemical properties? Tick **one** box.

☐ **A** They have the same number of shells of electrons.

☐ **B** They have the same number of outer shell electrons.

☐ **C** They all have at least one full inner shell of electrons.

☐ **D** The atoms of the elements are similar in size.

[1]

[Total 2 marks]

2 Mendeleev created an early version of the periodic table, in which he arranged the elements according to their atomic masses and their properties. Mendeleev left some gaps in his table. [Grade 6-7]

a) Explain why Mendeleev left gaps in his table.

....

....

[1]

b) Mendeleev used his table to predict the properties of undiscovered elements that would fit in the gaps he left. One of these was an element in Group 4, which Mendeleev called **eka-silicon**. **Figure 1** shows some properties of the Group 4 elements silicon and tin, plus some predictions about the properties of eka-silicon.

	Silicon (Si)	**Eka-silicon (Ek)**	**Tin (Sn)**
Atomic Mass	28	72	119
Density in g/cm³	2.3	?	7.3
Appearance	grey/silver non-metal	grey metal	grey metal
Formula of oxide	SiO_2	EkO_2	SnO_2
Formula of chloride	$SiCl_4$	?	$SnCl_4$
Reaction with acid	None	?	Slow

Figure 1

Use the information in **Figure 1** to predict the following properties of eka-silicon:

i) Density: ....

ii) Formula of chloride: ....

iii) Reaction with acid: ....

[3]

[Total 4 marks]

 ☐   ☐   ☐

Section 10 — Key Concepts in Chemistry

Electronic Configurations

1   The atomic number of neon is 10.   (Grade 6-7)

How many electrons does neon have in its **outer shell**?

☐ **A** 2   ☐ **C** 8

☐ **B** 6   ☐ **D** 10

[Total 1 mark]

2   The atomic number of sulfur is 16.   (Grade 6-7)

a) Write down the electronic structure of sulfur.

....
[1]

b) Draw a diagram to show how the electrons are arranged in a single sulfur atom.

[1]
[Total 2 marks]

3   Magnesium is found in group 2 and period 3 of the periodic table.   (Grade 6-7)

a) Explain how you could use this information to **deduce** the electronic structure of magnesium.

....

....

....

....

....
[3]

b) Give the electronic structure of magnesium.

....
[1]
[Total 4 marks]

Ions

The formulas of the ion formed by four mystery elements are shown below. Draw lines to match each of the ions to the correct description of the element that it was formed from.

A^+	A non-metal from Group 6
D^-	A metal from Group 2
X^{2+}	A metal from Group 1
Z^{2-}	A non-metal from Group 7

1 Ions can have either a positive or a negative charge. **Grade 6-7**

a) Describe what happens to an atom when it turns into a negative ion.

....
[1]

b) Magnesium is in Group 2 of the periodic table.

i) Predict what charge a magnesium ion will have.

....
[1]

ii) Magnesium has the atomic number 12.
Calculate the number of electrons found in one magnesium ion.

number of electrons = ...
[1]

[Total 3 marks]

2 Potassium can react with oxygen to form the ionic compound potassium oxide. **Grade 7-9**

a) Which of following shows the correct formula for potassium oxide?

☐ **A** KO   ☐ **B** KO_2 ☐ **C** K_2O ☐ **D** K_2O_2

[1]

b) The most common isotope of oxygen has an atomic number of 8 and a mass number of 16.
How many protons, neutrons and electrons would an oxide ion have?

protons = ...

electrons = ...

neutrons = ...

[3]

[Total 4 marks]

Section 10 — Key Concepts in Chemistry

Ionic Bonding

1 Ionic bonding is one of the three types of chemical bonds found in compounds. *Grade 4-6*

a) In which of the following compounds are the particles held together by ionic bonds?
Tick **one** box.

☐ **A** carbon dioxide   ☐ **C** nitrogen trichloride

☐ **B** calcium chloride   ☐ **D** nitrogen monoxide

[1]

b) **Figure 1** shows the formation of the ionic compound lithium chloride from its elements, but it is incomplete. Complete **Figure 1** by drawing an arrow to show the transfer of the electron, adding the charges of the ions and completing the chloride ion to show the electrons in its outer shell.

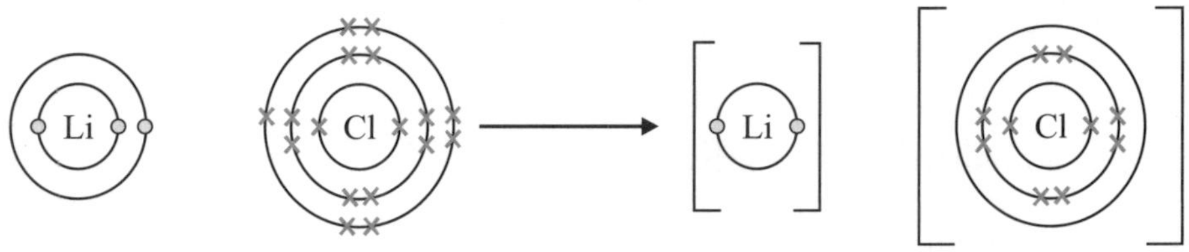

Figure 1

[3]

c) Name the force that holds the ions together in an ionic bond.

....

[1]

d) Suggest how you can tell from a dot and cross diagram that the particles in a compound are held together by ionic bonds.

....

....

[1]

[Total 7 marks]

2 Calcium fluoride, CaF_2, is an ionic compound. *Grade 6-7*

Draw a dot and cross diagram to show the bonding in calcium fluoride.
You should include the charges on the ions in your diagram.

[Total 4 marks]

Ionic Compounds

Circle the correct words or phrases below so that the statement is correct.

In an ionic compound, the particles are held together by weak/<u>strong</u> forces of attraction.

These forces act <u>in all directions</u>/<u>in one particular direction</u> which results in the particles

bonding together to form <u>giant lattices</u>/<u>small molecules</u>.

1   This question is about the structure and properties of ionic compounds.   Grade 4-6

   a) Which of the following properties is **not** typical for an ionic compound?
       Tick **one** box.

   ☐ **A** high boiling point   ☐ **C** high melting point

   ☐ **B** conduct electricity in the liquid state   ☐ **D** conduct electricity in the solid state

[1]

   b) Name the type of structure that ionic compounds have.

   ....

[1]

[Total 2 marks]

2   Sodium chloride is an ionic compound.   Grade 6-7

   a) Describe the structure of a crystal of sodium chloride. You should state:
       • What particles are present in the crystal.
       • How these particles are arranged.
       • What holds the particles together.

   ....

   ....

   ....

   ....

   ....

[4]

   b) Explain why sodium chloride has a high melting point.

   ....

   ....

[2]

[Total 6 marks]

3 Potassium bromide has a lattice structure that is similar to sodium chloride.

a) Complete **Figure 1** below to show the position and charge of the ions in potassium bromide. Write a symbol in each blank circle to show whether it is a potassium ion or a bromide ion.

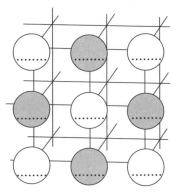

Figure 1

[3]

b) Give **one advantage** and **one disadvantage** of using the type of diagram above to represent the structure of an ionic compound.

Advantage: ....

Disadvantage: ....

[2]

c) State whether potassium bromide is likely to be **soluble** or **insoluble** in water.

....

[1]

[Total 6 marks]

4 **Figure 2** shows some data about the ionic compound lithium chloride. For each of the properties shown, explain how the structure of lithium chloride causes this property.

Boiling point / °C	Electrical conductivity of solid	Electrical conductivity of solution
1382	Low	High

Figure 2

Boiling point ....

....

....

Electrical conductivity of solid ....

....

Electrical conductivity of solution ....

....

[Total 6 marks]

Exam Practice Tip

Don't panic if you're asked about an ionic compound that you haven't met before. Think about what you <u>do</u> know about ionic compounds, and read the question carefully to make sure you've picked up on any extra information you've been given.

Covalent Bonding

1   This question is about the forces in simple molecular substances.   (Grade 4-6)

   a) Compare the strength of the bonds that hold the atoms in a molecule together with the forces that exist between different molecules.

....

....

[2]

   b) When a simple molecular substance melts, is it the bonds between atoms or the forces between molecules that are broken?

....

[1]

[Total 3 marks]

2   Silicon has the electronic structure 2.8.4.   (Grade 6-7)

     Use this information to predict how many covalent bonds one atom of silicon will form in a simple molecule. Explain your answer.

....

....

....

[Total 2 marks]

3   Nitrogen has the electronic structure 2.5. Chlorine has the electronic structure 2.8.7. Nitrogen trichloride, NCl_3, is a covalent compound. In each molecule of NCl_3, one nitrogen atom is covalently bonded to three chlorine atoms.   (Grade 6-7)

   a) Draw a dot and cross diagram to show the bonding in **one molecule** of nitrogen trichloride. You only need to include the outer shell electrons of each atom.

[3]

   b) Predict, with reasoning, whether nitrogen trichloride can conduct electricity.

....

....

[1]

[Total 4 marks]

Section 10 — Key Concepts in Chemistry

4 Hashim says: "Covalent bonds are very strong, so you need a lot of energy to separate the atoms in a covalent compound. This means simple molecular substances must have high melting and boiling points."

Grade 6-7

Is Hashim correct? Explain your answer.

....

....

....

....

....

....

[Total 3 marks]

5 Methane and poly(ethene) are both substances that are made up of molecules whose atoms are joined together by covalent bonds.

Grade 7-9

a) Briefly describe how the carbon and hydrogen atoms in methane, CH_4, bond to gain stable electronic structures.

....

....

....

....

[4]

b) What type of molecule is poly(ethene)?

....

[1]

c) At room temperature and pressure, methane is a gas, while poly(ethene) is a solid. Suggest why poly(ethene) has a higher boiling point than methane.

....

....

....

....

[4]

[Total 9 marks]

Exam Practice Tip

If you answered these questions correctly, then that's a pretty good sign that you know all about simple molecules and covalent bonding. But don't forget, that's only part of the story — you need to be able to compare simple molecular substances with all the other types of structure covered in this topic, such as ionic structures and giant covalent structures.

Giant Covalent Structures and Fullerenes

1 The diagrams below show two different types of carbon structure.

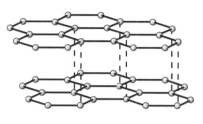

Figure 1

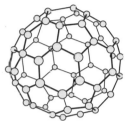

Figure 2

a) Name the two carbon structures shown.

   i) **Figure 1**: ....

   [1]

   ii) **Figure 2**: ....

   [1]

b) Both of the structures shown are able to conduct electricity.
   Explain why this is possible.

   ....

   ....

   ....

   [2]

c) Which of the two forms of carbon shown would you expect to have a **higher** melting point?
   Explain your answer.

   ....

   ....

   ....

   ....

   [3]

d) Name **one** other type of carbon structure, and draw a diagram below to show its bonding.

   Structure: ....

   [2]

   [Total 9 marks]

Section 10 — Key Concepts in Chemistry

Metallic Bonding

1 This question is about how the structure and bonding of metals affects their properties.

a) Draw a labelled diagram to show how the metal ions and
the electrons that take part in bonding are arranged in a metal.

[3]

b) Explain how the metal ions are held together in this arrangement.

....

....

[2]

c) i) State whether metals generally have high or low boiling points. Explain your answer.

....

....

[2]

ii) A student has samples of two solids, marked **A** and **B**. One is copper, a metallic element, and
the other is iodine, a non-metal element. Solid **A** has a melting point of 1085 °C and solid **B**
has a melting point of 114 °C. Suggest which of the solids is iodine and explain your answer.

....

....

[1]

d) Explain why metals are good conductors of electricity.

....

....

[2]

e) Explain how the structure of metals means they are able to be bent and shaped.

....

....

....

[2]

[Total 12 marks]

Exam Practice Tip

Metals have some really nifty properties, and being able to explain all the properties of metals requires you to be really
familiar with metallic bonding. Remember, it's because of those layers of positive metal ions and that sea of electrons that
metals behave the way they do. Make sure you're able to explain the bonding in metals and link it to their properties.

Conservation of Mass

1 A student mixes 3.0 g of silver nitrate solution and 15.8 g of sodium chloride solution together in a flask and seals it with a bung. The following precipitation reaction occurs:

$$AgNO_{3\,(aq)} + NaCl_{(aq)} \rightarrow AgCl_{(s)} + NaNO_{3\,(aq)}$$

Predict the total mass of the contents of the flask after the reaction. Explain your answer.

....

....

....

[Total 2 marks]

2 A student is investigating a reaction between zinc and hydrochloric acid.
The reaction produces hydrogen gas and a solution of zinc chloride.
The student's experimental set-up is shown in **Figure 1**.

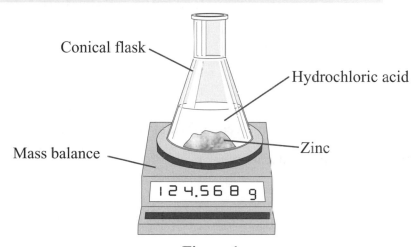

Conical flask

Hydrochloric acid

Mass balance

Zinc

1 2 4 . 5 6 8 g

Figure 1

a) How would you expect the mass of the conical flask and its contents
to change over the course of the reaction? Explain your answer.

....

....

....

[2]

b) The student repeats the reaction, but this time attaches a gas syringe to the top of the flask.
How would you expect the mass of the apparatus and its contents
to change over the course of the reaction? Explain your answer.

....

....

....

[2]

[Total 4 marks]

Relative Masses and Chemical Formulas

Match up the following formulas with the correct relative formula mass of the substance.

F_2	38
C_2H_6	40
CaO	30
NaOH	56

1 The compound butane-1,4-diamine has the molecular formula $C_4H_{12}N_2$. Which of the following is the empirical formula of butane-1,4-diamine?

☐ **A** C_2H_5N ☐ **B** $C_2H_6N_2$ ☐ **C** CH_3N ☐ **D** C_2H_6N

[Total 1 mark]

2 Decaborane is a compound with the molecular formula $B_{10}H_{14}$.

What is the empirical formula of decaborane?

empirical formula = ...

[Total 1 mark]

3 **Figure 1** shows the displayed formula of the compound dithionic acid.

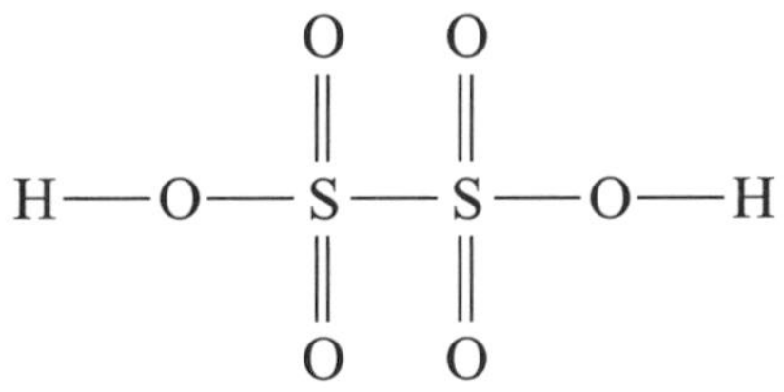

$$H-O-\overset{\displaystyle O}{\underset{\displaystyle O}{\overset{\|}{\underset{\|}{S}}}}-\overset{\displaystyle O}{\underset{\displaystyle O}{\overset{\|}{\underset{\|}{S}}}}-O-H$$

Figure 1

a) What is the molecular formula of this compound?
   Give your answer in the form $H_aS_bO_c$, where *a*, *b* and *c* are whole numbers.

....

[1]

b) What is the empirical formula of this compound?

empirical formula = ...

[1]

[Total 2 marks]

4 The formula of the compound barium nitrate is Ba(NO₃)₂. $\boxed{\text{Grade } 6\text{-}7}$

Find the relative formula mass of barium nitrate.

relative formula mass = ...

[2]

5 Oct-1-ene is a compound with the molecular formula C_8H_{16}. Emmy says the empirical formula of oct-1-ene is C_2H_4. $\boxed{\text{Grade } 6\text{-}7}$

Is Emmy correct? Explain your answer.

....

....

....

[Total 1 mark]

6 An oxide of an element, X, has the formula X_2O_3. The relative formula mass of X_2O_3 is 160. $\boxed{\text{Grade } 7\text{-}9}$

Calculate the relative atomic mass of element X.

relative atomic mass = ...

[Total 3 marks]

7 Compound Q has the empirical formula C_2HF. The relative formula mass of compound Q is 132. $\boxed{\text{Grade } 7\text{-}9}$

What is the molecular formula of compound Q?

molecular formula = ...

[Total 3 marks]

Section 10 — Key Concepts in Chemistry

Moles and Concentration

1 What is the approximate number of atoms in 1 mole of carbon atoms? *(Grade 4-6)*

☐ **A** 7.23×10^{23} atoms ☐ **C** 6.02×10^{-23} atoms

☐ **B** 7.23×10^{24} atoms ☐ **D** 6.02×10^{23} atoms

[Total 1 mark]

2 A student makes a saline solution by dissolving 36 g of sodium chloride in 0.40 dm³ of water. What is the concentration of the solution? *(Grade 4-6)*

☐ **A** 90 g dm⁻³ ☐ **B** 14.4 g dm⁻³ ☐ **C** 14 400 g dm⁻³ ☐ **D** 0.090 g dm⁻³

[Total 1 mark]

3 A pharmacist is synthesising aspirin, $C_9H_8O_4$, as part of a drugs trial. After the experiment, the pharmacist calculates that she has made 12.4 moles of aspirin. What mass of aspirin has the pharmacist made? *(Grade 4-6)*

The relative atomic mass, A_r, of C = 12, of H = 1 and of O = 16.

mass = ... g
[Total 2 marks]

4 How many atoms are there in 7 moles of ammonia, NH_3? Give your answer to 3 significant figures. *(Grade 6-7)*

.... atoms
[Total 2 marks]

5 A student makes up a volume of a standard solution of copper sulfate with a concentration of 75.0 g dm⁻³. He does this by dissolving powdered copper sulfate in 220 cm³ of water. *(Grade 6-7)*

Calculate the mass of copper sulfate that was used to make the solution.

mass = ... g
[Total 1 mark]

6 A student dissolves 56 g of potassium chloride in 400 cm³ of water. **Grade 6-7**

a) Calculate the concentration of the resultant potassium chloride solution in g dm⁻³.

concentration = ... g dm⁻³

[1]

b) The student wants to make a solution with the same concentration using only 300 cm³ of water. Use your answer from part a) to calculate the mass of potassium chloride that the student will need to add to this volume of water to create a solution with the same concentration.

mass = ... g

[1]

[Total 2 marks]

7 A lab technician is making up some solutions for students to use in some of their classes. **Grade 7-9**

a) The technician makes a standard solution of sodium hydroxide for a titration experiment. She makes 600 cm³ of the solution at a concentration of 52 g dm⁻³.

Calculate the number of moles of sodium hydroxide used to make the solution.
Relative formula mass, M_r, of NaOH = 40

number of moles = ...

[2]

b) i) The technician also makes a standard solution of sodium carbonate. The solution has a concentration of 80.0 g dm⁻³ and was made by adding 36.0 g of sodium carbonate to a volume of water. Calculate the volume of water, in cm³, that she used to make the solution.

volume of water = ... cm³

[2]

ii) For a separate experiment, the technician needs a sodium carbonate solution with a concentration of 40.0 g dm⁻³.
What can she do to her 80.0 g dm⁻³ solution to make it this concentration?

....

[1]

[Total 5 marks]

Section 10 — Key Concepts in Chemistry

8 A sample of an unknown element contains 1.204×10^{25} atoms.

Grade 7-9

a) How many moles of atoms of the element are in the sample?

number of moles = ...
[1]

b) Given that the atoms have a mean mass of 9.3×10^{-23} g, what is the identity of the element?

....
[2]
[Total 3 marks]

9 A student is investigating an unidentified acid, which is made up of oxygen, sulfur and hydrogen atoms.

Grade 7-9

a) Given that 3.5 moles of the acid has a mass of 343 g, what is the relative formula mass of the acid?

relative formula mass = ...
[1]

b) The percentage mass of the acid made up of oxygen atoms is 65%.
To the nearest whole number, how many moles of oxygen atoms are in one mole of the acid?

number of moles = ...
[2]

c) In one mole of the acid, there is one mole of sulfur atoms.
Deduce the chemical formula of the acid.

chemical formula = ...
[3]
[Total 6 marks]

Calculating Empirical Formulas

1 An oxide of lead contains 2.07 g of lead and 0.16 g of oxygen. What is the empirical formula of the lead oxide?

$A_r(Pb) = 207$, $A_r(O) = 16$

empirical formula = ...

[Total 2 marks]

2 53.66 g of an oxide of copper contains 10.8 g of oxygen by mass. Calculate the empirical formula of the copper oxide.

$A_r(Cu) = 63.5$, $A_r(O) = 16$

empirical formula = ...

[Total 3 marks]

3 83% of the mass of a certain hydrocarbon is made up of carbon atoms. Calculate the empirical formula of the hydrocarbon.

$A_r(C) = 12$, $A_r(H) = 1$

empirical formula = ...

[Total 3 marks]

4 A student carried out an experiment to calculate the empirical formula of an oxide of iron. She burnt 3.808 g of iron until it had all reacted. She found that the weight of the product was 5.440 g.

a) Suggest a piece of equipment that the student could use to carry out the reaction in.

....

[1]

b) Calculate the empirical formula of the iron oxide formed during the experiment.

$A_r(Fe) = 56$, $A_r(O) = 16$

empirical formula = ...

[3]

[Total 4 marks]

Limiting Reactants

Complete the following sentences by filling in the blanks with the words on the right.

1) If the amount of limiting reactant in a reaction is decreased,

then the amount of product made will ....

not change

2) If the amount of limiting reactant in a reaction is increased,

then the amount of product made will ....

decrease

3) If the amount of an excess reactant is increased,

then the amount of product made will ....

increase

1 James is investigating the reactivity of some metals. As part of his investigation, he places a piece of magnesium metal in a flask containing an excess of hydrochloric acid and monitors the reaction. The reaction produces hydrogen gas and a metal salt solution.

Grade 4-6

a) Which of the reactants is the limiting reactant?

....

[1]

b) James repeats the experiment but changes the starting quantities of magnesium and acid. He lets the reaction proceed to completion, and notes that once the reaction has finished, the reaction vessel contains a small amount of grey metal and a clear solution.

In this second experiment, what is the limiting reactant? Explain your answer.

....

....

....

[2]

[Total 3 marks]

2 An industrial process converts the alkene ethene into ethanol, according to the reaction below.

Grade 6-7

$$C_2H_4 + H_2O \rightarrow CH_3CH_2OH$$

What mass of ethanol can be made from 53 g of ethene, given that water is in excess?

mass = ... g

[Total 2 marks]

3 The following equation shows the complete combustion of ethane in air.

$$2C_2H_6 + 7O_2 \rightarrow 4CO_2 + 6H_2O$$

a) In a complete combustion reaction, some ethane reacted with exactly 128 g of oxygen. Calculate the mass of water produced. Give your answer to three significant figures.

mass = ... g

[3]

b) A company burns ethane to generate power for an industrial process.

As part of a carbon-reducing scheme, the company can only produce a maximum 4.4 tonnes of carbon dioxide per day (where 1 tonne = 1 000 000 g). What is the maximum mass, in tonnes, of ethane that the company can burn each day so as not to exceed the limit of carbon dioxide?

mass = ... tonnes

[3]

[Total 6 marks]

4 Urea, $(NH_2)_2CO$, is a compound that can be synthesised industrially using the following reaction.

$$2NH_3 + CO_2 \rightarrow (NH_2)_2CO + H_2O$$

a) A company makes 120.6 tonnes (where 1 tonne = 1 000 000 g) of urea each day. What mass of carbon dioxide, in tonnes, is required to make this mass of urea?

mass = ... tonnes

[3]

b) Usually the reaction happens in an excess of ammonia. However, a leak in a pipe means the mass of ammonia entering the reaction chamber on one day is reduced to 59.5 tonnes.

What is the decrease, in tonnes, in the amount of urea produced on this day?

decrease in mass = ... tonnes

[4]

[Total 7 marks]

Section 10 — Key Concepts in Chemistry

Balancing Equations Using Masses

1 Viola reacts 200 g of a metal, **X**, with oxygen. The result of the reaction is 280 g of a single product, which is an oxide of metal **X**.

a) What mass of oxygen was used in the reaction?

mass = ... g

[1]

b) Given that Viola's reaction produced 5 moles of X oxide,
write a balanced symbol equation for the reaction of **X** with oxygen.
$A_r(X) = 40$, $A_r(O) = 16$

....

[4]

[Total 5 marks]

2 1.0 g of warm sodium was added to a gas jar containing 1.0 g of chlorine gas (Cl_2). They reacted to form sodium chloride. The equation for the reaction is $2Na + Cl_2 \rightarrow 2NaCl$. Determine which reactant was the **limiting reactant** in this reaction.

$A_r(Na) = 23$, $M_r(Cl_2) = 71$

....

[Total 3 marks]

3 A scientist gently heats tin and iodine together. They react to form a single product, which is a metal halide. Given that 3.57 g of tin reacts exactly with 15.24 g of iodine, write a balanced equation for this reaction.

$A_r(Sn) = 119$, $M_r(I_2) = 254$, M_r (metal halide) = 627

....

[Total 5 marks]

Section 10 — Key Concepts in Chemistry

States of Matter

Warm-Up

Identify which of the following statements is **false**. Tick **one** box.

Particles in liquids are free to move past each other but tend to stick together. ☐

Particles of a substance in the liquid state have more energy
than particles of the same substance in the solid state. ☐

There is hardly any force of attraction between particles in gases. ☐

Particles in liquids are held in fixed positions by strong forces. ☐

1   Substances can exist in three states of matter: solid, liquid or gas.   *Grade 4-6*

a)   In which of these three states of matter are the forces of attraction between the particles **strongest**?

....

[1]

b)   Name the state of matter illustrated in **Figure 1**.

Figure 1

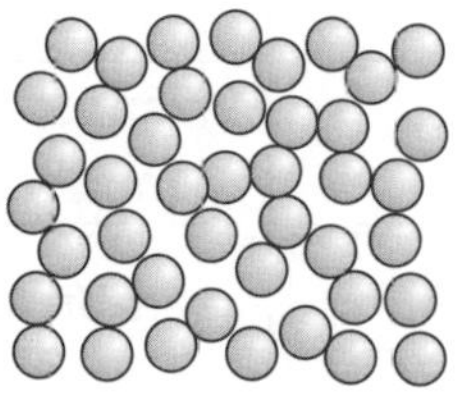

....

[1]

[Total 2 marks]

2   A student has a sample of a solid substance.
She heats it gradually until it turns into a liquid.   *Grade 6-7*

Describe the differences between the particles in the substance when it is in
the liquid state and when it is in the solid state. Give your answer in terms
of the movement of the particles and the amount of energy that they have.

....

....

....

....

....

[Total 3 marks]

Changes of State

1   The equations below show four processes that use water as a starting material.

     A: $H_2O_{(l)} \rightarrow H_2O_{(s)}$ **B**: $2H_2O_{(l)} + 2Na_{(s)} \rightarrow 2NaOH_{(aq)} + H_{2\,(g)}$

     C: $H_2O_{(l)} \rightarrow\; + H_2O_{(g)}$ **D**: $2H_2O_{(l)} \rightarrow 2H_{2\,(g)} + O_{2\,(g)}$

a)   State which equation shows evaporation.

     ....

[1]

b)   State which **two** equations show chemical changes and explain your answer.

     ....

     ....

[2]

[Total 3 marks]

2   **Figure 1** shows some properties of four elements.

Figure 1

Name	Melting point / °C	Boiling point / °C	Appearance		
			solid	liquid	gas
fluorine	−220	−188	colourless	bright yellow	pale yellow
mercury	−39	357	silvery metallic	silvery metallic	n/a
bromine	−7	59	red-brown	red-brown	orange
rubidium	39	688	silvery-white metallic	silvery-white metallic	n/a

During an experiment, samples of each of these four elements were placed in separate test tubes. All four test tubes were then gradually cooled together, from 25 °C to −200 °C.

Describe what you would expect to observe during the experiment as it progressed. In your answer you should describe what you think will happen to each sample.

     ....

     ....

     ....

     ....

     ....

     ....

     ....

     ....

[Total 4 marks]

Purity

1 Misty-Marie is doing a chemistry experiment.
The instructions say she needs to use pure water.
Stanley offers her a bottle labelled '100% Pure Spring Water'.

Grade
4-6

Suggest why Stanley's water is unlikely to be suitable for Misty-Marie's experiment.

....

....

....

....

[Total 2 marks]

2 Copper can be made extremely pure. The melting points of two samples
of copper were measured. Sample **A** had a melting point of 1085 °C
and sample **B** melted over the range 900 – 940 °C.

Grade
4-6

Suggest which of the samples, **A** or **B**, was the **most pure**. Explain your answer.

....

....

....

[Total 2 marks]

3 A scientist is comparing samples of two substances.
One sample is a pure compound, but the other is a mixture.
Both substances are solids at room temperature.

Grade
4-6

a) The scientist decides to work out which is the pure compound by heating both
samples and recording their melting points. Explain how she will be able to tell
which is the pure compound, even if she does not know its melting point.

....

....

....

[2]

b) Suggest what apparatus the scientist could use to
measure the melting points of the substances in the lab.

....

[1]

[Total 3 marks]

Section 11 — States of Matter and Mixtures

Separating Mixtures

1   **Figure 1** shows a set of equipment you could use for separating a mixture in the lab.

Figure 1

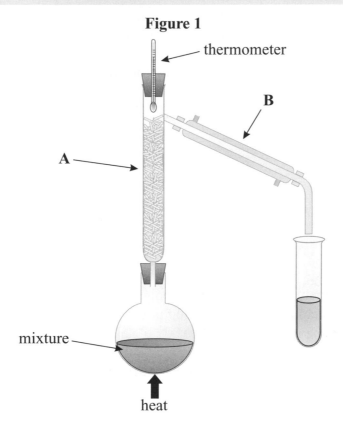

a) Name the pieces of equipment labelled **A** and **B**.

   i) **A**: ....

   [1]

   ii) **B**: ....

   [1]

b) i) What is the name of the separation method this equipment would be used for?

   ....

   [1]

   ii) Describe what type of mixture you would use this method to separate.

   ....

   ....

   [2]

   iii) Reuben is using this method to separate a mixture.
        His mixture contains a substance that is flammable.
        Suggest a suitable piece of equipment that he could use to heat the mixture.

   ....

   [1]

   [Total 6 marks]

2* A student wants to separate the components of a mixture.
The mixture is a white powder composed of barium sulfate and potassium iodide.
Figure 2 shows some information about the two compounds in the mixture.

Figure 2

Name	Melting point / °C	Boiling point / °C	Appearance at room temperature	Soluble in water?
barium sulfate	1580	1600	white solid	no
potassium iodide	681	1330	white solid	yes

Describe a detailed method that the student could use
to obtain pure samples of **both** compounds.

....

....

....

....

....

....

....

....

....

....

....

....

....

....

....

....

....

[Total 6 marks]

Section 11 — States of Matter and Mixtures

3   Sodium chloride dissolves in water, but not in ethanol.
    Sodium chloride has a melting point of 801 °C and a boiling point of 1413 °C.
    Ethanol has a melting point of −114 °C and a boiling point of 78 °C.

a) Suggest a purification method which would separate a mixture of sodium chloride and ethanol,
    but **not** a mixture of sodium chloride and water. Explain your answer.

    ....

    ....

    ....

    ....

                                                                                                                    [3]

b) Suggest a purification method which would separate a mixture of sodium chloride and water
    and would **also** separate a mixture of sodium chloride and ethanol. Explain your answer.

    ....

    ....

    ....

                                                                                                                    [2]
                                                                                           [Total 5 marks]

4   **Figure 3** lists the boiling points of three compounds.

Grade 7-9

Figure 3

Name	Formula	Boiling point / °C
cyclopentane	C_5H_{10}	49
cyclohexane	C_6H_{12}	81
ethyl ethanoate	$C_4H_8O_2$	77

Suggest why a mixture of cyclohexane and ethyl ethanoate might be more difficult to separate
than a mixture of cyclohexane and cyclopentane.

    ....

    ....

    ....

    ....

                                                                                           [Total 2 marks]

Exam Practice Tip
You might find some of these separation techniques cropping up in questions about other practicals — you often need to
use one of them at the end of an experiment to separate out a pure sample of the product from the reaction mixture.

Chromatography

1 Olivia analysed an unknown mixture of liquids using paper chromatography. The solvent she used was ethanol. The chromatogram she produced is shown in **Figure 1**.

Figure 1

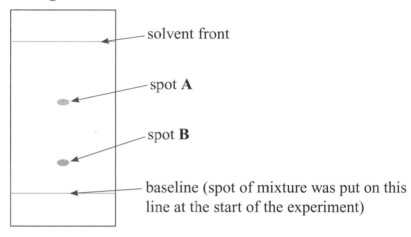

solvent front

spot **A**

spot **B**

baseline (spot of mixture was put on this line at the start of the experiment)

a) Name the mobile phase in Olivia's experiment

....
[1]

b) What does this chromatogram tell you about the number of components in the mixture? Explain your answer.

....

....
[2]

c) Calculate the R_f value of spot **B**. Use a ruler to help you.

$$R_f = \frac{\text{distance travelled by solute}}{\text{distance travelled by solvent}}$$

$R_f = $ ....
[3]

d) Olivia is given a list of five chemicals. She is told that her mixture is made up of a combination of some of the chemicals on the list. Explain how Olivia could use pure samples of the chemicals on the list to identify the components of the mixture using paper chromatography.

....

....

....

....
[2]

[Total 8 marks]

Section 11 — States of Matter and Mixtures

2   Lamar wants to analyse the composition of a sample of ink.
The ink is made up of a number of dyes dissolved in a solvent.

a) The boiling point of the solvent is lower than the boiling point of any of the dyes.

   i) Suggest a method Lamar could use to separate the mixture of dyes from the solvent.

   ....

   [1]

   ii) Explain how this method can provide data that could help Lamar to identify the solvent.

   ....

   ....

   [1]

b) Lamar uses paper chromatography to analyse the mixtures of dyes in the ink.
He compares the mixture with five different water soluble dyes, A to E.
After 30 minutes, the chromatogram in **Figure 2** was obtained.

Figure 2

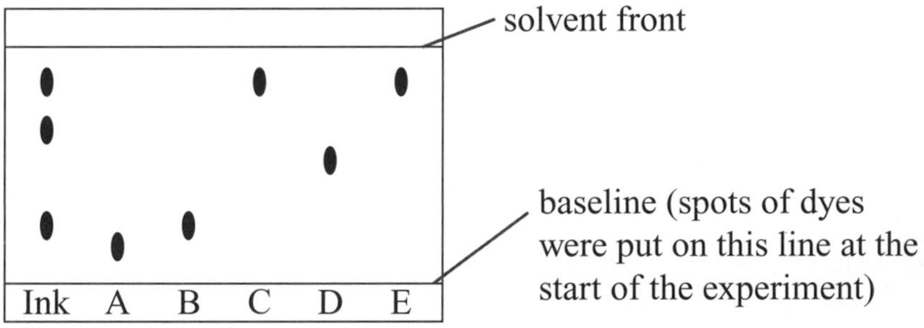

solvent front

baseline (spots of dyes
were put on this line at the
start of the experiment)

Ink   A   B   C   D   E

Outline the procedure for setting up and running this experiment.

   ....

   ....

   ....

   ....

   ....

   ....

   [5]

c) Explain the results shown on Lamar's chromatogram.

   ....

   ....

   ....

   ....

   ....

   ....

   [4]

   [Total 11 marks]

Water Treatment

Warm-Up

Tick the boxes to show whether the following statements are **true** or **false**.

	True	False
Potable water is the same as drinking water.	☐	☐
Potable water can only be produced from fresh water found in rivers, streams and reservoirs.	☐	☐
Ordinary tap water can be used in chemical analysis.	☐	☐

1   This question is about potable water.   (Grade 4-6)

a)   Name **one** source of water used in the production of potable water in the UK.

....

[1]

b)   Potable water can be produced by distilling sea water.
Explain why this method is not used to produce potable water in the UK.

....

....

[2]

[Total 3 marks]

2   A purification plant uses multiple steps to purify water.   (Grade 6-7)

a)   When the water arrives at a water purification plant, it is passed through wire meshes and gravel beds to remove large solid impurities. Give the name of this step.

....

[1]

b)   Some water purification plants use aluminium sulfate to carry out a sedimentation step.
How does the aluminium sulfate contribute to the purification process?

....

....

[1]

c)   The purification process ends with chlorination.
Describe what happens to the water during this process and state why it is carried out.

....

....

[2]

[Total 4 marks]

Section 11 — States of Matter and Mixtures

Acids and Bases

Warm-Up

Circle the statements below that are **true**.

As H^+ concentration increases, pH decreases.

Acids contain lots of OH^- ions.

Neutral substances have a pH of 8.

Alkalis turn Universal indicator blue/purple.

Acids have pHs of less than 7.

Alkalis are soluble bases.

1 This question is about acids and bases.
Figure 1 shows the pH values of some everyday substances. Grade 4-6

Figure 1

Substance	pH
Beer	4
Bicarbonate of soda	9
Milk	7

a) Write the name of the substance in **Figure 1** that is an acid.

....

[1]

b) What colour would you expect to see if phenolphthalein was added to bicarbonate of soda solution?

....

[1]

c) Which ion is produced by an acid in aqueous solution? Tick **one** box.

- [ ] **A** Cl^-
- [ ] **B** H^+
- [ ] **C** OH^-
- [ ] **D** OH^+

[1]

[Total 3 marks]

2 Which of the following equations shows a neutralisation reaction? Tick **one** box. Grade 4-6

- [ ] **A** $HNO_3 + LiOH \rightarrow LiNO_3 + H_2O$
- [ ] **B** $Mg + H_2O \rightarrow MgO + H_2$
- [ ] **C** $Na_2O + H_2O \rightarrow 2NaOH$
- [ ] **D** $C_4H_{10} + 6\frac{1}{2}O_2 \rightarrow 4CO_2 + 5H_2O$

[Total 1 mark]

3 Acids and bases react together in neutralisation reactions. (Grade 4-6)

a) Write the general word equation for a neutralisation reaction between an acid and a base.

....

[1]

b) In terms of hydrogen ions and hydroxide ions, write an ionic equation
for a neutralisation reaction in aqueous solution.

....

[1]

[Total 2 marks]

4 Kevin has samples of three different alkaline solutions. Solution **A** has a pH of 11, (Grade 6-7)
solution **B** has a pH of 13 and solution **C** has a pH of 8. State which of Kevin's
solutions has the **lowest** concentration of hydroxide ions and explain your answer.

....

....

....

[Total 2 marks]

5 Haifa is investigating the properties of a (Grade 6-7)
sample of dilute hydrochloric acid, HCl.

PRACTICAL

a) She puts 100 cm³ of the acid into a flask.
Suggest a piece of apparatus that Haifa could use to accurately measure out 100 cm³ of the acid.

....

[1]

b) Haifa adds a measured mass of powdered calcium hydroxide to the flask. It reacts completely.
She takes a sample of the resultant solution and tests its pH using universal indicator paper.

i) Suggest what colour the universal indicator paper will turn
when Haifa adds a spot of the solution. Explain your answer.

....

....

[3]

ii) Haifa repeats the same procedure several times. After she adds the fifth lot of calcium
hydroxide, she sees a small amount of unreacted solid left at the bottom of the flask.
Suggest what colour the universal indicator paper will turn at this point. Explain your answer.

....

....

[3]

[Total 7 marks]

Section 12 — Chemical Changes

Strong and Weak Acids

1 Tamal has two beakers, each containing a sample of a different acid.
The acid in beaker X is **stronger** than the acid in beaker Y.
The acid in beaker Y is **more concentrated** than the acid in beaker X.

Which row of the table in **Figure 1** could describe the contents of the two beakers? Tick **one** box.

Figure 1

	Beaker X	Beaker Y
☐ **A**	0.002 mol/dm^3 HCl	4.0 mol/dm^3 CH$_3$COOH
☐ **B**	4.0 mol/dm^3 HCl	0.002 mol/dm^3 CH$_3$COOH
☐ **C**	0.002 mol/dm^3 CH$_3$COOH	4.0 mol/dm^3 HCl
☐ **D**	4.0 mol/dm^3 CH$_3$COOH	0.002 mol/dm^3 HCl

[Total 1 mark]

2 Methanoic acid, HCOOH, is a **weak acid**.

a) Explain what is meant by the term 'weak acid'.

....

....

[1]

b) Write a chemical equation to show how methanoic acid acts as a weak acid.

....

[2]

[Total 3 marks]

3 Jackie is carrying out an experiment to measure how
the pH of a strong acid is affected by its concentration.

a) Jackie takes a sample of an acidic solution, A, made by dissolving a solid acid in deionised water.
He wants to make his sample of the acid more concentrated.
Which of the following things could he do? Tick **one** box.

☐ **A** Add a more dilute solution of the acid to the sample.

☐ **B** Add more water to the sample.

☐ **C** Add more solution the same as A to the sample.

☐ **D** Dissolve more solid acid in the sample.

[1]

b) At a certain dilution, the hydrogen ion concentration is 0.001 mol/dm^3 and the acid has a pH of 3.
Jackie increases the concentration of hydrogen ions in the sample to 0.1 mol/dm^3.
What is the new pH of the acid?

....

[1]

[Total 2 marks]

Reactions of Acids

1 June reacts a metal and an acid together in a flask. Which of the following describes the products of this reaction? Tick **one** box. *(Grade 4-6)*

- [ ] **A** A salt and water.
- [ ] **B** A salt and carbon dioxide gas.
- [ ] **C** A salt, water and carbon dioxide gas.
- [ ] **D** A salt and hydrogen gas.

[Total 1 mark]

2 Complete **Figure 1** to show the chemical formulas of the salts created in the reactions involving the following acids. *(Grade 6-7)*

Figure 1

	Hydrochloric acid (HCl)	Nitric acid (HNO$_3$)	Sulfuric acid (H$_2$SO$_4$)
Zinc metal (Zn)	ZnCl$_2$	....	ZnSO$_4$
Calcium carbonate (CaCO$_3$)	CaCl$_2$	Ca(NO$_3$)$_2$	....
Sodium hydroxide (NaOH)	NaCl	NaNO$_3$	....
Potassium carbonate (K$_2$CO$_3$)	....	KNO$_3$	K$_2$SO$_4$

[Total 4 marks]

3 Pauline mixes zinc carbonate, ZnCO$_3$, with hydrochloric acid, HCl, and notes that the mixture starts to bubble as a gas is given off. *(Grade 6-7)*

a) Give the name of the gas that is responsible for the bubbles in the reaction. Describe a test you could perform to identify this gas.

....

....

[3]

b) Write a balanced chemical equation for the reaction between hydrochloric acid and zinc carbonate.

....

[2]

c) What is the name of the salt produced by the reaction?

....

[1]

[Total 6 marks]

Making Insoluble Salts

1   Insoluble salts can be made by precipitation reactions.
     Which of the following equations describes a precipitation reaction? Tick **one** box.

Grade
4-6

☐   **A** $CuO_{(s)} + 2HCl_{(aq)} \rightarrow CuCl_{2\ (aq)} + H_2O_{(l)}$

☐   **B** $HCl_{(aq)} + NaOH_{(aq)} \rightarrow NaCl_{(aq)} + H_2O_{(l)}$

☐   **C** $2HNO_{3\ (aq)} + ZnCO_{3\ (s)} \rightarrow Zn(NO_3)_{2\ (aq)} + H_2O_{(l)} + CO_{2\ (g)}$

☐   **D** $Pb(NO_3)_{2\ (aq)} + 2NaCl_{(aq)} \rightarrow PbCl_{2\ (s)} + 2NaNO_{3\ (aq)}$

[Total 1 mark]

2   Jerry is making a sample of silver chloride, an insoluble salt, by mixing two salt solutions.

Grade
6-7

a)   Suggest two salt solutions that Jerry could mix to make silver chloride.

....

....

[1]

b)   Once Jerry has made the salt, he pours the whole
     solid and salt solution into a filter funnel, as shown in **Figure 1**.

Figure 1

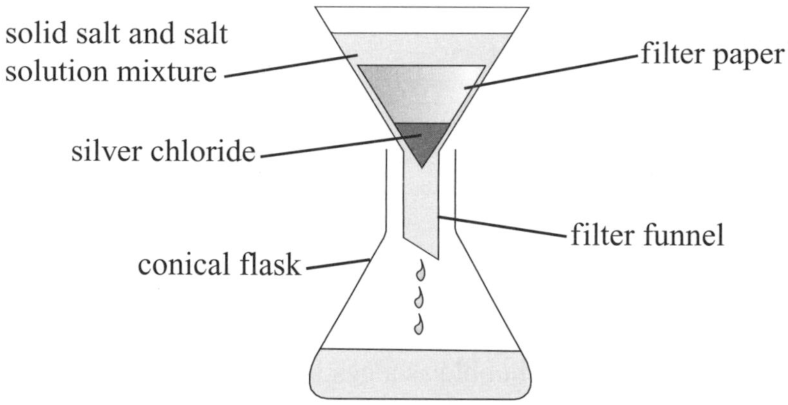

solid salt and salt
solution mixture ———   ——— filter paper

silver chloride ———

                                                 ——— filter funnel

conical flask ———

What has Jerry done wrong? Explain how this could affect
the mass of solid salt that he collects from the solution.

....

....

....

[2]

c)   After Jerry has isolated the salt, he washes it with deionised water.
     Explain why he uses deionised water as opposed to tap water.

....

....

[1]

[Total 4 marks]

3 The students in a chemistry class are investigating the properties of calcium salts. Grade 6-7

a) They plan to carry out reactions to make calcium nitrate, $Ca(NO_3)_2$, and calcium sulfate, $CaSO_4$. Before they start, four students predict whether the salts will be soluble or insoluble. Which prediction is correct? Tick **one** box.

☐ **A** Ashley: "Both calcium salts will be insoluble."

☐ **B** Benni: "Both reactions will make soluble calcium salts."

☐ **C** Chen: "We'll get an insoluble precipitate of calcium sulfate, but calcium nitrate is soluble in water."

☐ **D** Dermot: "Calcium sulfate dissolves in water, but calcium nitrate doesn't, so only calcium nitrate will form as a precipitate."

[1]

b) In a third reaction, the students want to produce the insoluble salt calcium carbonate, $CaCO_3$. Suggest two soluble salts they could react together to make a precipitate of calcium carbonate.

....

....

[2]

[Total 3 marks]

4 Davina reacts aqueous iron(III) nitrate solution, $Fe(NO_3)_3$, with aqueous sodium hydroxide solution, NaOH, to make an insoluble salt containing iron. Grade 6-7

a) Write down the chemical formula of the insoluble salt.

....

[1]

b) Davina used the following method to prepare the salt:

1. Mix the sodium hydroxide solution with the iron(III) nitrate solution in a beaker and stir.
2. Line a filter funnel with filter paper and place it in a conical flask. Pour the contents of the beaker into the filter paper.
3. Rinse the beaker with deionised water and tip this into the filter paper.
4. Rinse the contents of the filter paper with deionised water.

i) Explain why Davina rinsed the beaker and added the rinsings to the filter paper.

....

[1]

ii) After completing step 4, Davina wants to dry the solid product. Suggest how she could do this.

....

[1]

iii) Given that Davina used an excess of iron(III) nitrate solution, state which **three** ions will be present in the solution that is left in the conical flask at the end of the experiment.

....

[2]

[Total 5 marks]

Section 12 — Chemical Changes

Making Soluble Salts

Nina is making the soluble salt zinc chloride by reacting zinc with hydrochloric acid.
She wants to prepare a pure, dry sample of solid zinc chloride.
The equipment Nina has available is listed below.
Circle the pieces of equipment below that you would expect Nina to use.

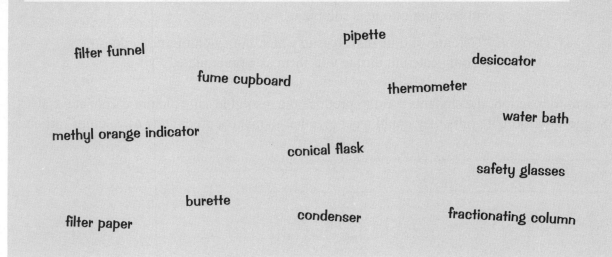

pipette

filter funnel

desiccator

fume cupboard

thermometer

water bath

methyl orange indicator

conical flask

safety glasses

burette

condenser

fractionating column

filter paper

---

1   The following steps are parts of a method you could use to produce
a pure, dry sample of the soluble salt magnesium sulfate, $MgSO_4$,
from solid magnesium hydroxide and sulfuric acid.

Grade
6-7

 1   Slowly heat the solution to evaporate off some of the water.

 2   Filter the solid off and dry it in a desiccator.

 3   Filter out the excess solid using a filter funnel and filter paper.

 4   Add magnesium hydroxide to a flask containing warm sulfuric acid.
       Continue adding the magnesium hydroxide until no more reacts
       (at this point, the excess solid will just sink to the bottom of the flask).

 5   Leave the solution to crystallise.

a) Which is the correct order that these steps should be carried out in? Tick **one** box.

☐   **A** 4, 1, 3, 2, 5

☐   **B** 1, 4, 2, 5, 2

☐   **C** 4, 3, 1, 5, 2

☐   **D** 3, 1, 2, 5, 4

[1]

b) Write a balanced symbol equation, including state symbols, that describes the
reaction between magnesium hydroxide, $Mg(OH)_2$, and sulfuric acid, H_2SO_4.

....

[3]

[Total 4 marks]

2 Andy is making a sample of potassium sulfate by reacting potassium hydroxide, KOH, and sulfuric acid, H_2SO_4, together.

Grade 6-7

a) Potassium sulfate is a soluble salt. Explain what is meant by the term soluble in this context.

....

[1]

b) Write a balanced chemical equation for this reaction.

....

[2]

c) Andy uses a titration method to add a potassium hydroxide solution to the acid until he reaches the end point, which is shown by a change in colour of an indicator in the solution. He then crystallises the solution to obtain the salt. Will this produce a pure sample of the salt? Explain your answer.

....

....

[1]

[Total 4 marks]

3 Copper sulfate is a soluble salt that can be made by the reaction between sulfuric acid, H_2SO_4, and copper oxide, CuO.

Grade 7-9

PRACTICAL

a) Write a balanced chemical equation for the reaction between sulfuric acid and copper oxide.

....

[2]

b)* Outline how you could prepare a pure, dry sample of copper sulfate in the lab from sulfuric acid and copper oxide.

....

....

....

....

....

....

....

....

....

....

[6]

[Total 8 marks]

Electrolysis

1 As part of an industrial process, a sample of potassium chloride, KCl, was electrolysed. *(Grade 4-6)*

a) Before the potassium chloride is electrolysed, it either has to be molten or dissolved in solution. Explain why this is necessary.

....

....

[2]

b) During the electrolysis of molten potassium chloride, potassium ions are reduced to potassium metal. At which electrode would you expect this reaction to occur?

....

[1]

[Total 3 marks]

2 Electrolysis is carried out on a solution of copper chloride, $CuCl_2$, using inert electrodes. *(Grade 6-7)*

a) Which of the following ions is **not** present in the solution? Tick **one** box.

☐ **A** H^+ ☐ **B** H_2O^- ☐ **C** Cl^- ☐ **D** Cu^{2+}

[1]

b) What would you expect to see happen at:

i) the anode? ....

ii) the cathode? ....

[2]

[Total 3 marks]

3 A solution of sodium chloride, NaCl, is electrolysed using platinum electrodes. *(Grade 6-7)*

a) Platinum electrodes are an example of inert electrodes.
Explain what is meant by the term 'inert' when referring to electrodes.

....

[1]

b) The sodium chloride solution contains dissolved sodium chloride and water only. List the ions that are present in solution during the electrolysis of sodium chloride solution using inert electrodes.

....

[2]

c) Write balanced half equations to show the reactions that occur at:

i) the anode ....

ii) the cathode ....

[4]

[Total 7 marks]

4 The half-equation for the reaction at the cathode during an electrolysis experiment is $Pb^{2+} + 2e^- \rightarrow Pb$. The half-equation for the reaction at the anode is $2I^- \rightarrow I_2 + 2e^-$.　**Grade 6-7**

a) Give the definition of the term **electrolyte**.

....

[2]

b) Give the chemical formula of the electrolyte in this experiment, given that it's a molten ionic compound.

....

[1]

[Total 3 marks]

5* A student is investigating the electrolysis of sodium chloride solution using inert electrodes. Describe how you would set up an electrochemical cell to carry out this investigation and predict what you would observe happening at each electrode as the reaction progressed.　**Grade 6-7**

....

....

....

....

....

....

....

....

....

[Total 6 marks]

6 When sodium sulfate solution is electrolysed using inert electrodes, sodium is not discharged at the cathode.　**Grade 7-9**

a) Explain why sodium **is not** discharged at the cathode and state what product **is** discharged instead.

....

....

[3]

b) State which **two** products are discharged at the anode.

....

[2]

c) Suggest an alternative electrolysis experiment that could be carried out that **would** produce sodium metal at the cathode.

....

[2]

[Total 7 marks]

Section 12 — Chemical Changes

7   Marco is investigating the electrolysis of copper sulfate. He sets up two cells as shown in **Figure 1**. In cell A, Marco uses platinum electrodes. In cell B, he uses pure copper electrodes. The cells are identical in all other respects.

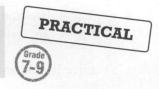

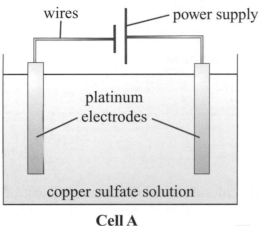
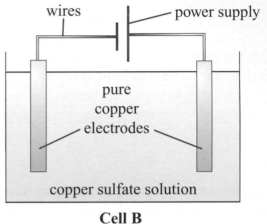

Figure 1

a) Both cells are turned on and left for 1 hour. Given that the masses of the two cells were the same at the start of the electrolysis, how would you expect them to compare after 1 hour? Explain your answer. Use appropriate half equations to justify your conclusion.

....

....

....

....

....

....

[6]

b) A similar cell to cell B can be used to purify copper. Give **one** similarity and **one** difference between the cell used to purify copper in industry and cell B.

....

....

[2]

[Total 8 marks]

8   Write half-equations to show what reactions occur at the cathode and the anode when acidified water is electrolysed.

Cathode: ....

Anode: ....

[Total 4 marks]

Exam Practice Tip

It's important to remember that when you electrolyse aqueous solutions (rather than molten salts) what products are made will depend on the reactivity of all the ions present in the solution. Make sure you've learnt which ions will be discharged from which solutions. And get plenty of practice at writing half-equations too — they're really important...

Reactivity Series and Reactivity of Metals

1   The reaction that occurs when a metal is burnt in oxygen can be described as an oxidation reaction. Explain why, using ideas about the transfer of oxygen.   **Grade 4-6**

....

....

....

[Total 2 marks]

2   Metals can be placed in order of reactivity based on how vigorously they react with water.   **Grade 4-6**

a) Write a word equation for the reaction of sodium with water.

....

[1]

b) Explain, using ideas about oxidation, why iron reacts much more slowly with cold water than sodium does.

....

....

[1]

[Total 2 marks]

3   Some metals can react with water.   **Grade 6-7**

a) i) Complete the symbol equation below for the reaction of calcium and water. Include state symbols.

$$Ca_{(s)} + 2H_2O_{(l)} \rightarrow \text{.......................} + \text{.........................}$$

[2]

ii) Identify which element is oxidised. Explain your answer in terms of oxygen.

....

....

[2]

iii) Suggest a metal which will react more vigorously with water than calcium. Explain your answer.

....

....

[2]

b) Put the metals sodium, zinc and potassium in order, based on how vigorously you think they would react with water.

Most vigorous .... Least vigorous

[1]

[Total 7 marks]

4 Which of the statements below about metal reactivity is **incorrect**? Tick **one** box. (Grade 6-7)

☐ **A** The easier it is for a metal atom to form a positive ion, the less reactive it will be.

☐ **B** The more resistant a metal atom is to oxidation, the less reactive it will be.

☐ **C** In a reactivity series, you will find a reactive metal above a less reactive metal.

☐ **D** The more reactive a metal is, the faster its reaction with water will be.

[Total 1 mark]

5 Amal performed some experiments to investigate the reactivity of metals. (Grade 6-7)

a) First, Amal placed pieces of four different metals into dilute hydrochloric acid.
Figure 1 shows what the four experiments looked like after 1 minute.

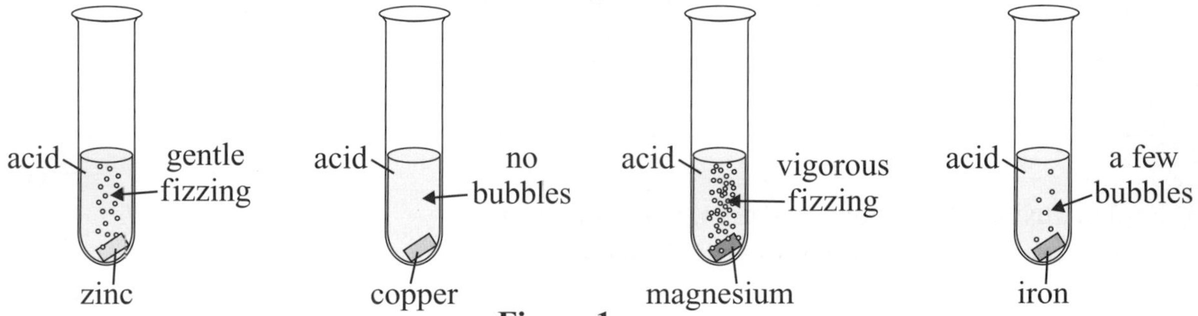

acid — gentle fizzing — zinc
acid — no bubbles — copper
acid — vigorous fizzing — magnesium
acid — a few bubbles — iron

Figure 1

Use **Figure 1** to put these metals in order of reactivity, starting with the **most reactive**.

....

[1]

b) Next, Amal was given samples of three mystery metals, marked **X**, **Y** and **Z**. She put small pieces of each of the metals in cold water. If there was no reaction with cold water, she tested the metal to see if it would react with steam. Her results are shown in **Figure 2**.

Metal	Any reaction with cold water?	Any reaction with steam?
X	Reacts vigorously. Hydrogen gas is produced.	
Y	no reaction	Reacts vigorously. Metal is coated with a white solid. Hydrogen gas is produced.
Z	no reaction	no reaction

Figure 2

i) Metal **Y** was zinc. It reacted with the steam to produce hydrogen gas and a white solid.
Name the white solid that was produced by this reaction.

....

[1]

ii) One of the other metals Amal was given was sodium.
Suggest whether sodium was metal **X** or metal **Z**. Give a reason for your answer.

....

....

[1]

[Total 3 marks]

Section 13 — Extracting Metals and Equilibria

Displacement Reactions

1 A student carries out a displacement reaction by reacting magnesium with an aqueous solution of iron chloride to produce magnesium chloride and iron.

$$Mg_{(s)} + FeCl_{2(aq)} \rightarrow MgCl_{2(aq)} + Fe_{(s)}$$

Explain why this displacement reaction is an example of a redox reaction.

....

....

[Total 2 marks]

2 Shaun adds small pieces of some metals to metal salt solutions. He records whether or not any reaction has taken place. His table of results is shown in **Figure 1**.

	Magnesium	Silver	Aluminium	Lead
Magnesium chloride	no reaction	no reaction	no reaction	no reaction
Silver nitrate	magnesium nitrate and silver formed	no reaction	aluminium nitrate and silver formed	lead nitrate and silver formed
Aluminium chloride	magnesium chloride and aluminium formed	no reaction	no reaction	no reaction
Lead nitrate	magnesium nitrate and lead formed	no reaction	aluminium nitrate and lead formed	no reaction

Figure 1

a) Shaun says "My results show that lead is more reactive than silver."
Do you agree? Explain your answer.

....

....

[1]

b) Construct a balanced symbol equation for the reaction between magnesium and aluminium chloride, $AlCl_3$.

....

[2]

c) Nickel is above lead in the reactivity series. Nickel is a shiny grey metal and nickel nitrate is green in solution. Lead is a dull grey metal and lead nitrate is colourless in solution. Suggest what Shaun would observe if he added nickel to lead nitrate solution.

....

....

....

[2]

[Total 5 marks]

Section 13 — Extracting Metals and Equilibria

Extracting Metals Using Carbon

1 The method used to extract metals from their ores can be determined using the reactivity series. Part of the reactivity series is shown in **Figure 1**.

Potassium	K	Most Reactive
Calcium	Ca	
Aluminium	Al	
Carbon	C	
Zinc	Zn	
Tin	Sn	
Copper	Cu	Least Reactive

Figure 1

a) Give the definition of a metal ore.

....

....

[1]

b) Suggest how copper is extracted from its ore in industry.

....

....

[1]

c) State **one** other metal from **Figure 1** that can be extracted in the same way as copper.

....

[1]

[Total 3 marks]

2 Iron is extracted from its ore, iron oxide (Fe_2O_3), in a blast furnace using carbon. Grade 7-9

a) Write a balanced equation for this reaction.

....

[2]

b) A certain batch of iron ore that contains impurities of zinc oxide and calcium oxide is reacted in a blast furnace. After the reaction is complete, any metal produced by the reaction was removed. Any unreacted ore was left in the reaction vessel.

The iron metal product was tested for purity and was found to contain traces of another metal. Suggest an identity for the other metal. Explain why it is present.

....

....

....

....

[3]

[Total 5 marks]

Other Methods of Extracting Metals

1 Aluminium is a metal that is widely used in construction. It can be extracted from its ore, aluminium oxide.

(Grade 4-6)

a) What is the name given to the technique used to extract aluminium from its ore?

....

[1]

b) As part of the extraction process, aluminium oxide is mixed in cryolite. What is the purpose of mixing the aluminium oxide with cryolite?

....

[1]

c) Pure aluminium is more expensive to buy than many metals which are extracted from their ores by reduction with carbon. Explain how the extraction process contributes to the higher cost of pure aluminium.

....

....

....

[2]

[Total 4 marks]

2 The increasing demand and the limited supply of metal-rich ores means that scientists are now developing new ways to extract metal from low-grade ores.

(Grade 6-7)

a) Describe how phytoextraction is used to extract some metals from their ores.

....

....

....

....

....

[4]

b) Give **one** advantage and **one** disadvantage of using phytoextraction to extract metals from their ores.

....

....

....

[2]

c) Name one other biological method of extracting metals from low-grade ores.

....

[1]

[Total 7 marks]

Section 13 — Extracting Metals and Equilibria

Recycling

1 This question is on recycling. (Grade 6-7)

a) An alternative to recycling is disposing of waste into landfill.
Give **one** disadvantage associated with using landfill to dispose of waste.

....

[1]

b) Avoiding using landfill is one environmental advantage of recycling. Give **two** other
environmental reasons why recycling is considered more sustainable than making new materials.

....

....

[2]

c) Give **two** economic benefits of recycling.

....

....

[2]

[Total 5 marks]

2 Rachel is sorting some rubbish that has accumulated around her house. (Grade 6-7)

a) Rachel has three pieces of rubbish made from three different materials, **A**, **B** and **C**.
Some data about the materials is shown in **Figure 1**.

Material	Availability of resource	Energy to recycle	Energy to extract
A	Abundant	High	Low
B	Limited	Low	High
C	Limited	Medium	High

Figure 1

From the data given, which material in **Figure 1** is the **best** to recycle? Explain your answer.

....

....

....

....

[2]

b) Rachel is able to recycle plastic bottles at her local recycling centre.
Given that many parts of the manufacturing process involve using fractions of crude oil,
explain why it is important to recycle plastics.

....

....

[1]

[Total 3 marks]

Life Cycle Assessments

A company is developing a new product. Identify the factors that they should consider when producing a life cycle assessment. Tick **two** boxes.

Colour of the product ☐   Demand for the product ☐

Recyclability of the product ☐   Attractiveness of the product ☐

Source of raw materials ☐   Profitability of the product ☐

1 A furniture company is designing a new range of chairs for children. They need to decide whether the chairs will be made out of polypropene or timber. (Grade 6-7)

a) The company carries out a life cycle assessment of both possible products. Describe the purpose of a life cycle assessment.

....

....

[1]

b) Some data about the two materials are shown in **Figure 1**.

Material	Source	Relative Energy Cost to Make/Extract	Cost
Timber	Trees	1	Medium
Poly(propene)	Crude oil	15	Low

Figure 1

Use the data in **Figure 1** to explain which material would be the **best** choice to make the chairs from, in terms of sustainability. Explain your answer.

....

....

....

....

....

[3]

c) Suggest **two** factors, other than those given in **Figure 1**, that the company should consider in their life cycle assessment when deciding whether to make the chairs from timber or polypropene.

....

....

[2]

[Total 6 marks]

2 A garden tool company is considering the environmental costs of producing a rake.

Grade 6-7

a) The rake contains components made from iron.
Suggest **two** environmental problems associated with extracting iron from its ore.

....

....

[2]

b) The rake contains parts that cannot be recycled, so the company thinks
that it is likely to be disposed of in landfill at the end of its life span.
Give **one** disadvantage of disposing of waste using landfill.

....

[1]

c) The rake is sold in plastic packaging.
Suggest a sustainable way that consumers could dispose of the packaging.

....

[1]

[Total 4 marks]

3 A toy company is carrying out a life cycle assessment of four prototype toys.
Figure 2 displays some of the data from their assessments.

Grade 7-9

Toy	CO$_2$ emissions (kg)	Solvent use (dm^3)	Energy consumption (MJ)
A	16.2	3981	267.84
B	14.8	2672	212.26
C	14.9	3876	159.82
D	12.4	2112	174.56

Figure 2

Using the data in the table, evaluate the relative environmental impact of producing each toy.

....

....

....

....

....

....

[Total 4 marks]

Exam Practice Tip

You may be given data and asked to figure out which product has the biggest or smallest environmental impact. It's
likely that there won't be an obvious answer at first glance — some products may have really low CO$_2$ emissions but
may pollute lots of water. You'll have to look at <u>all</u> the factors and decide which product is the best or worst overall.

Dynamic Equilibrium

Warm-Up

Complete the paragraph below by circling the correct option from the choices.

The Haber Process is <u>an irreversible / a reversible</u> reaction that forms <u>ammonia / sulfuric acid</u> from hydrogen and nitrogen. The nitrogen used in the process is extracted from <u>the air / crude oil</u> and the hydrogen is extracted from <u>the air / natural gas</u>.

The conditions used for the Haber Process are a temperature of <u>200 °C / 450 °C</u>, a pressure of <u>250 atm / 200 atm</u> and in the presence of an <u>iron / aluminium</u> catalyst.

---

1 Dynamic equilibrium can only be achieved in reversible reactions. *(Grade 4-6)*

a) Compare the rates of the forwards and backwards reactions at dynamic equilibrium.
   State how this affects the concentrations of reactants and products present at dynamic equilibrium.

   ....

   ....

   [2]

b) Dynamic equilibrium can only be reached in a closed system.
   Explain what is meant by a 'closed system'.

   ....

   ....

   [1]

c) During a certain reversible reaction, the equilibrium lies to the left. How should the
   concentration of the reactants be altered in order to increase the rate of product formation?

   ....

   [1]

   [Total 4 marks]

---

2 An aqueous solution of blue copper(II) ions can react with chloride ions to form a yellow copper compound. The ionic equation for this reaction is: $Cu^{2+} + 4Cl^- \rightleftharpoons [CuCl_4]^{2-}$ *(Grade 6-7)*

a) What does the symbol '$\rightleftharpoons$' mean in this reaction?

   ....

   [1]

b) A solution containing copper(II) ions is mixed with a solution containing chloride ions in a flask.
   The solution quickly turns green. When observed for a few minutes no further change in colour
   can be seen. Explain these observations.

   ....

   ....

   ....

   [2]

   [Total 3 marks]

Section 13 — Extracting Metals and Equilibria

Le Chatelier's Principle

1 The equilibrium position of a reaction is dependent on the conditions that the reaction is carried out under.

Grade 4-6

a) What does Le Chatelier's Principle say about the effect of changing the conditions of a reversible reaction at equilibrium?

....

[1]

b) State **two** conditions you could change in order to alter the position of equilibrium of a reaction that happens in solution.

....

....

[2]

[Total 3 marks]

2 Methanol can be manufactured industrially from a gas mixture of carbon monoxide and hydrogen in the following reaction: $CO_{(g)} + 2H_{2(g)} \rightleftharpoons CH_3OH_{(g)}$. This occurs over a Cu-ZnO-Al_2O_3 catalyst, under conditions of 250 °C and 50–100 atm. The forward reaction is exothermic.

Grade 6-7

a) Under a certain set of conditions, the equilibrium lies to the right. Describe what this means, in terms of the concentration of products and reactants.

....

....

[1]

b) Identify which of the following statements is **false**. Tick **one** box.

☐ **A** A decrease in the concentration of CO shifts the position of equilibrium to the left.

☐ **B** Increasing the concentration of H_2 shifts the position of equilibrium to the right.

☐ **C** Increasing the temperature to 470 °C shifts the position of equilibrium to the left.

☐ **D** The Cu-ZnO-Al_2O_3 catalyst shifts the position of equilibrium to the right.

[1]

c) Amara says, to increase the yield of the reaction, they should decrease the pressure of the reaction. Russell disagrees. Which student do you agree with? Explain your answer.

....

....

....

....

[2]

[Total 4 marks]

3 A mixture of iodine monochloride (ICl) and chlorine is sealed in a gas syringe.
The gases react in a reversible reaction to form iodine trichloride (ICl_3) and eventually
reach an equilibrium. The equation for the reaction is: $ICl_{(g)} + Cl_{2(g)} \rightleftharpoons ICl_{3(s)}$.

Grade 7-9

a) Given that the forward reaction is exothermic, explain how the relative quantities of ICl and ICl_3
would change if the mixture was heated, and all other conditions remained the same.

....

....

....

[2]

b) Explain how the relative quantities of ICl and ICl_3 would change if the plunger were pushed into
the syringe, and the temperature remained constant.

....

....

....

[3]

[Total 5 marks]

4 Dinitrogen tetroxide (N_2O_4) is a colourless gas. It decomposes in a reversible reaction to
form the brown gas, nitrogen dioxide (NO_2). The reaction equation is: $N_2O_{4(g)} \rightleftharpoons 2NO_{2(g)}$.

Grade 7-9

a) When a sample of N_2O_4 is left to decompose in a sealed tube, a pale brown colour can be seen.
If this mixture is heated, the colour becomes a darker brown. Explain this observation and predict
whether the forward reaction is exothermic or endothermic.

....

....

....

[3]

b) Explain how you would expect the colour of the equilibrium mixture to change if
the pressure of the mixture is decreased, and all other conditions are kept the same.

....

....

....

....

[3]

[Total 6 marks]

Exam Practice Tip

Working out what happens to the position of an equilibrium when you change the conditions can be a bit of a brain
twister. Just remember that for any change that's made, the reaction will try to do the opposite. So if you increase the
temperature the endothermic reaction will speed up, if you increase the pressure the equilibrium will move to the side
where there are fewer moles of gas, and if you increase the concentration of a reactant you'll get more products.

Section 13 — Extracting Metals and Equilibria

Group 1 — Alkali Metals

1 The alkali metals are found in Group 1 of the periodic table. (Grade 4-6)

a) Which of the following statements is the **best** description of the alkali metals? Tick **one** box.

☐ **A** Soft metals with relatively high melting points.

☐ **B** Soft metals with relatively low melting points.

☐ **C** Hard metals with relatively high melting points.

☐ **D** Hard metals with relatively low melting points.

[1]

b) The alkali metals readily react to form ionic compounds.
Explain why their ions usually have a charge of +1.

....

....

[2]

[Total 3 marks]

2 A teacher is demonstrating the reactions between water and some alkali metals to her class. In one reaction, she adds a small piece of potassium to cold water. (Grade 6-7)

a) Name the **two** products of this reaction.

....

[2]

b) Describe what you would expect to see if a small piece of potassium was added to cold water.

....

....

....

....

[2]

c) It is **not** safe to carry out the reaction between rubidium and water in the laboratory.
Explain why this is the case, using ideas about the electronic configurations of Group 1 metals.

....

....

....

....

....

[3]

[Total 7 marks]

Group 7 — Halogens

Which of the following statements about the halogens is **true**? Tick **one** box.

☐ They are non-metals that exist as single atoms.

☐ They are metals that exist as single atoms.

☐ They are non-metals that exist as molecules of two atoms.

☐ They are metals that exist as molecules of two atoms.

1   Amelia is testing gases.   (Grade 4-6)

Figure 1 shows a gas being tested.

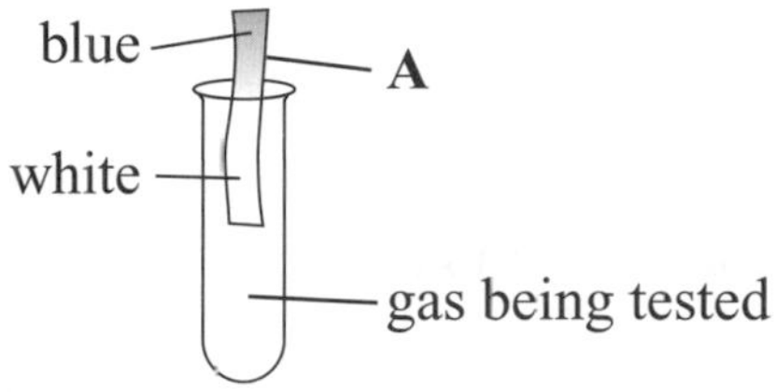

Figure 1

a)   Identify the item labelled **A** in **Figure 1**.

....

[1]

b)   Suggest which gas was present in the test tube.

....

[1]

[Total 2 marks]

2   The halogens can react with alkali metals to form metal halide salts.   (Grade 4-6)

a)   Name the metal halide salt that will be formed when the following pairs of elements react.

   i)   Bromine and sodium.

....

[1]

   ii) Iodine and potassium.

....

[1]

b)   When chlorine gas reacts with lithium, the salt lithium chloride, LiCl, is formed.
Write the balanced symbol equation for this reaction.

....

[2]

[Total 4 marks]

3 A chemist is carrying out some reactions involving halogens. (Grade 6-7)

a) i) In his first experiment he reacts hydrogen gas with chlorine gas.
Write a balanced chemical equation for this reaction.

....

[2]

ii) The chemist dissolves the product of this reaction in water and adds universal indicator.
What colour will the solution turn? Explain your answer.

....

....

[2]

b) The chemist carries out another reaction at room temperature and pressure, using a different gaseous halogen. Determine which of the halogens he must be using. Explain your answer.

....

....

[2]

c) Describe the appearance of bromine at room temperature.

....

[2]

[Total 8 marks]

4 The reactivity of halogens is dependent on their electronic configuration. (Grade 7-9)

a) Describe the electronic configuration of the halogens and how it changes down Group 7.

....

....

....

[2]

b) Sodium reacts violently with fluorine, at room temperature, to form sodium fluoride.
Predict how astatine might react with sodium at room temperature. Explain your answer.

....

....

....

....

....

[3]

[Total 5 marks]

Exam Practice Tip

One of the most important things to learn about Group 7 elements is the trend you find in reactivity as you go down or up the group. And you need to be able to explain this trend using the electronic structure of the halogens. Smashing.

Halogen Displacement Reactions

1   Josie investigated the reactions that occur when chlorine, bromine or iodine are added to different sodium halide solutions. **Figure 1** shows her results.

	Sodium chloride solution ($NaCl_{(aq)}$, colourless)	Sodium bromide solution ($NaBr_{(aq)}$, colourless)	Sodium iodide solution ($NaI_{(aq)}$, colourless)
Add chlorine water ($Cl_{2(aq)}$, colourless)	no reaction	solution turns orange	....
Add bromine water ($Br_{2(aq)}$, orange)	no reaction	....	solution turns brown
Add iodine water ($I_{2(aq)}$, brown)	no reaction	no reaction	no reaction

Figure 1

a) Use your knowledge of the reactivity trend of the halogens to fill in the missing results in **Figure 1**.

[2]

b) Explain why there was no reaction when Josie added iodine water to sodium bromide solution.

....

....

[2]

c) i) Construct a balanced symbol equation for the reaction that happened when Josie added chlorine water to sodium bromide solution.

....

[2]

ii) Explain, in terms of electrons, why the reaction between chlorine water and sodium bromide solution can be described as a redox reaction.

....

....

....

[2]

d) Astatine is below iodine in Group 7. Predict whether chlorine water would react with sodium astatide solution. Explain your answer.

....

....

[2]

[Total 10 marks]

Group 0 — Noble Gases

1   Old-style filament light bulbs contain a thin metal filament. If these light bulbs were filled with air, oxygen would react with the filament causing it to burn away. To avoid this, the light bulbs are filled with argon.

Explain why argon is suitable for this use, including ideas about electronic structure.

....

....

....

....

[Total 3 marks]

2   The noble gases are inert gases that make up Group 0 of the periodic table.

Figure 1 shows some information about the first four noble gases.

Element	Symbol	Boiling point (°C)	Density (kg m⁻³)
Helium	He	−269	0.18
Neon	Ne	−246	0.90
Argon	Ar	−186	?
Krypton	Kr	−153	3.7

Figure 1

a) i) The element below krypton in Group 0 is xenon.
        Use the information in **Figure 1** to predict what the boiling point of xenon will be.

boiling point = ... °C

[1]

ii) Use the information in **Figure 1** to predict the density of argon.

density = ... kg m⁻³

[1]

b) Would you expect the boiling point of radon to be higher or lower than the boiling point of xenon? Explain your answer.

....

....

[1]

[Total 3 marks]

Exam Practice Tip

Make sure you get lots of practice at questions like Q2, where you're given information about some of the elements in a group and asked to use it to predict something about another element in the group. They need careful thinking through.

Reaction Rate Experiments

1   A scientist reacts hydrochloric acid with marble chips to form calcium chloride, water and carbon dioxide gas.   **PRACTICAL**

a)   He decides to measure the volume of carbon dioxide formed to work out the rate of the reaction. Outline a method the scientist could follow to monitor the volume of gas produced over the course of the reaction.

....

....

....

....

[3]

b)   **Figure 1** shows a graph of his results. On **Figure 1**, sketch a curve that shows how the volume of gas produced would change over time if the experiment was carried out at a higher temperature.

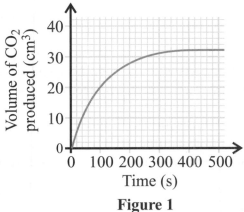

Figure 1   *[2]*

c)   The scientist repeated the reaction using different quantities of reactants. Reaction **X** used 0.500 g of marble chips and an excess of 0.100 mol dm^{-3} hydrochloric acid. Using **Figure 2**, determine which of the following sets of conditions could have resulted in reaction **Y**. Tick **one** box.

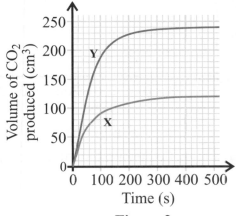

Figure 2

☐   **A** 0.250 g of marble chips and an excess of 0.100 mol dm^{-3} hydrochloric acid.

☐   **B** 1.00 g of marble chips and an excess of 0.100 mol dm^{-3} hydrochloric acid.

☐   **C** 0.250 g of marble chips and an excess of 0.200 mol dm^{-3} hydrochloric acid.

☐   **D** 1.00 g of marble chips and an excess of 0.200 mol dm^{-3} hydrochloric acid.   *[1]*

[Total 6 marks]

2 Laiza is investigating the effect of temperature on the rate of the reaction between sodium thiosulfate and hydrochloric acid. The reaction forms a cloudy, yellow precipitate of sulfur.

a) She measures out volumes of both reactants and gently heats each of the solutions in a water bath to 50 °C. Outline a method that Laiza could follow to monitor the rate of this reaction.

....

....

....

[3]

b) Laiza repeats the experiment but instead heats both reactant solutions to 30 °C.

i) How would you expect the rate of this reaction to compare to the rate of the reaction at 50 °C?

....

[1]

ii) Name **one** factor Laiza would have to keep the same for both reactions to make it a fair test.

....

[1]

[Total 5 marks]

3 Shabnam reacted magnesium ribbons with hydrochloric acid. As the reaction proceeded, hydrogen gas was produced.

Shabnam carried out two different reactions, **M** and **N**, using two different concentrations of acid in order to see how concentration affects the rate of reaction. All of the other variables were kept the same during both of the experiments. A graph of her results is shown in **Figure 3**.

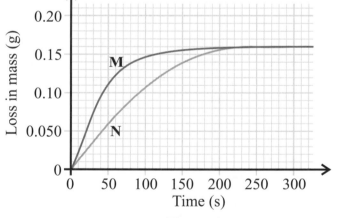

Figure 3

a) Which reaction, **M** or **N**, used a higher concentration of hydrochloric acid. Explain your answer.

....

....

[2]

b) Using the graph, calculate the rate of reaction **N** between 0 and 50 seconds.

rate = ... g s^{-1}

[2]

[Total 4 marks]

4 A student wanted to calculate the rate of reaction between nitric acid and zinc. He carried out two experiments under the same conditions, but in one he used zinc ribbons and in the other he used zinc powder.

The graph in **Figure 4** shows the rate of reaction for both experiments, labelled **Q** and **R**.

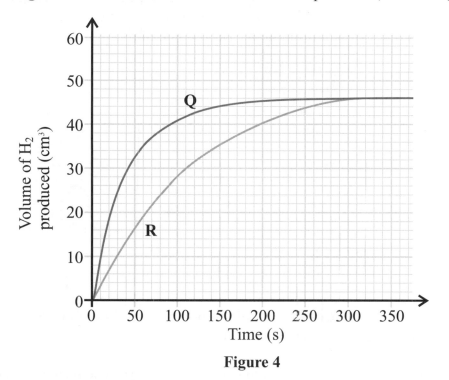

Figure 4

a) i) Calculate the rate of reaction **Q** at 50 seconds. Give your answer to 2 significant figures.

rate = ... $cm^3 \ s^{-1}$

[3]

ii) Calculate the rate of reaction **R** at 120 seconds. Give your answer to 2 significant figures.

rate = ... $cm^3 \ s^{-1}$

[3]

b) State which reaction, **Q** or **R**, used the powdered zinc. Explain your answer.

....

....

....

[3]

[Total 9 marks]

Exam Practice Tip

Drawing a tangent at a specific point on a curve can be quite tricky. You need to make sure that it has the same gradient as the curve at that specific point. Drawing a tangent too different from the correct gradient could make a big difference to your final answer, so take your time and try moving your ruler around a bit first to find the best position.

Collision Theory

A student is investigating the reaction between nitric acid and calcium carbonate under three different conditions, **A**, **B** and **C**. All other variables are kept the same. Circle the condition that will result in the greatest rate of reaction.

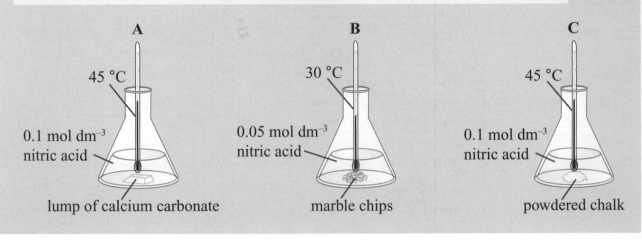

A	B	C
45 °C	30 °C	45 °C
0.1 mol dm^{-3} nitric acid	0.05 mol dm^{-3} nitric acid	0.1 mol dm^{-3} nitric acid
lump of calcium carbonate	marble chips	powdered chalk

1 This question is about the rate of a chemical reaction between two reactants, one of which is in solution, and one of which is a solid.

a) Which of the following changes would **not** cause the rate of the chemical reaction to increase? Tick **one** box.

☐ **A** Increasing the concentration of the solution.

☐ **B** Heating the reaction mixture to a higher temperature.

☐ **C** Using a larger volume of the solution, but keeping the concentration the same.

☐ **D** Grinding the solid reactant so that it forms a fine powder.

[1]

b) What is the name given to the minimum amount of energy which particles must have if they are to react when they collide?

....

[1]

[Total 2 marks]

2 This question is about the rate of the reaction between magnesium and hydrochloric acid. The chemical equation for the reaction is:

$$Mg_{(s)} + 2HCl_{(aq)} \rightarrow MgCl_{2(aq)} + H_{2(g)}$$

Using collision theory, explain why cutting the magnesium into smaller pieces affects the rate of this reaction.

....

....

....

[Total 2 marks]

3 The Sabatier reaction can be used industrially to make methane from carbon dioxide and hydrogen in the following reaction:
Grade 6-7

$$CO_{2(g)} + 4H_{2(g)} \rightarrow CH_{4(g)} + 2H_2O_{(g)}$$

a) How could the pressure be altered to **increase** the rate of the reaction?

....

[1]

b) Use the collision theory to explain how this pressure change causes the rate to increase.

....

....

....

[2]

[Total 3 marks]

4 Horatio and Sharon are carrying out an experiment. They each react 50 cm³ of 0.300 mol dm⁻³ sodium thiosulfate with 5.0 cm³ of 2.000 mol dm⁻³ hydrochloric acid.
Grade 6-7

a) Horatio carries out his reaction at room temperature. Sharon heats her reactants to 45 °C and carries out the reaction in a 45 °C water bath. Horatio thinks that his reaction will have taken place much more quickly than Sharon's reaction. Is Horatio correct? Explain your answer using collision theory.

....

....

....

....

....

[3]

b) i) Sharon repeats her experiment using different concentrations of hydrochloric acid. Which of the following concentrations of hydrochloric acid would result in the **slowest** rate of reaction? Tick **one** box.

☐ **A** 0.350 mol dm⁻³ hydrochloric acid

☐ **B** 1.250 mol dm⁻³ hydrochloric acid

☐ **C** 2.100 mol dm⁻³ hydrochloric acid

☐ **D** 0.550 mol dm⁻³ hydrochloric acid

[1]

ii) Explain your answer.

....

....

[2]

[Total 6 marks]

Section 15 — Rates of Reaction and Energy Changes

Catalysts

1 Enzymes are a type of catalyst. (Grade 4-6)

a) Identify which of the following catalysts is an example of an enzyme. Tick **one** box.

☐ **A** Iron: a catalyst used in the Haber process.

☐ **B** Manganese(IV) oxide: a catalyst used in the decomposition of hydrogen peroxide.

☐ **C** RuBisCO: a catalyst used in photosynthesis.

☐ **D** Vanadium pentoxide: a catalyst used in the Contact process.

[1]

b) Give **one** example of when enzymes are used as catalysts in industrial processes.

....

[1]

[Total 2 marks]

2 Zola is observing the decomposition of hydrogen peroxide. The reaction is very slow. Meredith tells her to repeat the experiment with manganese(IV) oxide powder, and the rate of reaction increases. (Grade 6-7)

a) Zola determines that the manganese(IV) oxide must have acted as a catalyst. Explain how a catalyst works to increase the rate of reaction.

....

....

....

[2]

b) Why does Zola only need to use a small mass of manganese(IV) oxide powder to catalyse the reaction?

....

[1]

c) The reaction profiles for both the catalysed and the uncatalysed reactions are shown in **Figure 1**. Identify what each of the labels, A–D, show.

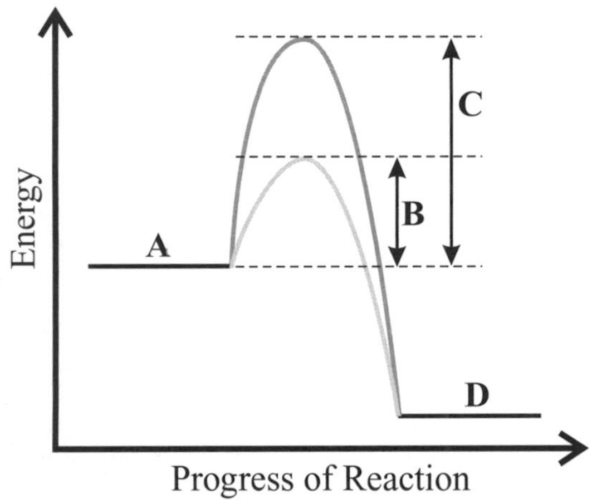

A: ....

B: ....

....

C: ....

....

D: ....

[4]

Figure 1

[Total 7 marks]

Endothermic and Exothermic Reactions

1 Which of the following energy changes describes an exothermic reaction? Tick **one** box.

		Energy of products	**Temperature of surroundings**
	A	Greater than reactants	Increases
	B	Less than reactants	Increases
	C	Greater than reactants	Decreases
	D	Less than reactants	Decreases

[Total 1 mark]

2 The thermal decomposition of calcium carbonate is an endothermic reaction.

Sketch and label a reaction profile for this reaction on the axes below. Label the activation energy.

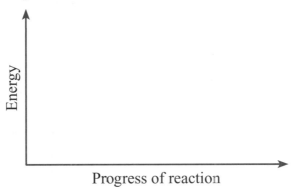

[Total 3 marks]

3 A company is looking for a reaction with a low activation energy to use in a hand warmer. The reaction profiles for the reactions being investigated are shown in **Figure 1**.

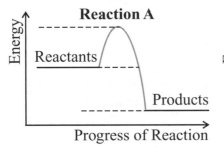 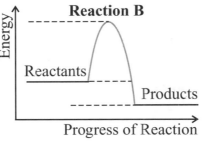 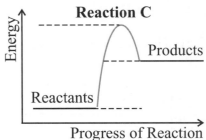

Figure 1

a) Define 'activation energy'.

....

....

[1]

b) Suggest which reaction would be **most suitable** for using in a hand warmer. Explain your answer.

....

....

....

[3]

[Total 4 marks]

Measuring Temperature Changes

1   A student is investigating the temperature change that occurs when he dissolves the same number of moles of two different salts, **A** and **B**, in water.

Grade 6-7

a) Suggest **three** essential pieces of apparatus needed for the investigation.

....

....

[3]

b)* Describe a method that the student could use to carry out his investigation.
    Include details of any variables that would need to be controlled.

....

....

....

....

....

....

....

....

[6]

c) The student's results are shown in **Figure 1**. Complete the table.

Salt	Initial temperature (°C)	End temperature (°C)	Temperature change (°C)
A	21.0	16.0	....
B	21.0	26.5	....

Figure 1

[2]

d) Which of the statements below about the student's experiment is correct? Tick **one** box.

☐ **A** Both salts dissolved exothermically.

☐ **B** Salt A dissolved exothermically, but salt B dissolved endothermically.

☐ **C** Salt A dissolved endothermically, but salt B dissolved exothermically.

☐ **D** Both salts dissolved endothermically.

[1]

[Total 12 marks]

Section 15 — Rates of Reaction and Energy Changes

Bond Energies

Which of the following statements is true? Tick **one** box.

☐ A During exothermic reactions, the energy taken to break the bonds in the reactants
is greater than the energy released by making the bonds in the products.

☐ B During endothermic reactions, the energy released by breaking bonds in
the reactants is less than the energy taken to make the bonds in the products.

☐ C During exothermic reactions, the energy taken to break the bonds in the reactants
is less than the energy released by making the bonds in the products.

☐ D During endothermic reactions, the energy taken to break the bonds in the
reactants is less than the energy released by making the bonds in the products.

1 Look at **Figure 1**. It shows the bond energies of some bonds.

Bond	Bond energy (kJ mol⁻¹)
C — H	413
C — O	358
H — O	463
C = C	614
C — C	347

Figure 1

a) Use **Figure 1** to work out the energy change of the
following reaction between ethene and water.

$$H_2C=CH_2 \; + \; H-O-H \; \rightarrow \; H-CH_2-CH_2-O-H$$

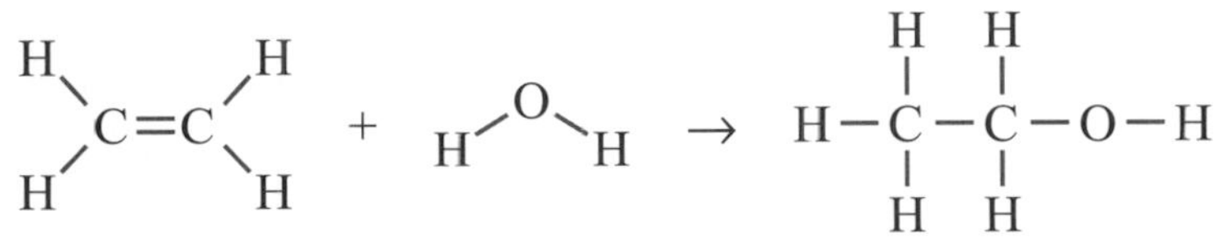

Energy change = ... kJ mol⁻¹

[3]

b) Using your answer to a), state whether the reaction between ethene and water
is endothermic or exothermic. Explain your answer.

....

....

[2]

[Total 5 marks]

2   The energy change of the following reaction is −119 kJ mol⁻¹.

$$H-\underset{\underset{H}{|}}{\overset{\overset{H}{|}}{C}}-\underset{\underset{H}{|}}{\overset{\overset{H}{|}}{C}}-H \;\; + \;\; Cl-Cl \;\; \rightarrow \;\; H-\underset{\underset{H}{|}}{\overset{\overset{H}{|}}{C}}-\underset{\underset{H}{|}}{\overset{\overset{Cl}{|}}{C}}-H \;\; + \;\; H-Cl$$

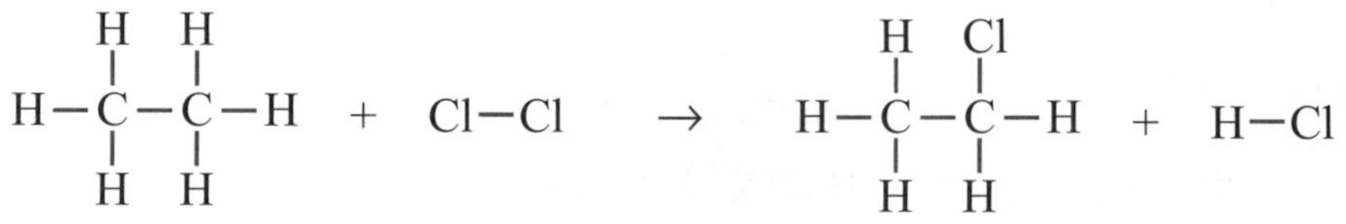

a) Compare the energy released by forming bonds in the products
in this reaction with the energy used to break bonds in the reactants.

....

....

[1]

b) Use this information, as well as the data in **Figure 2**,
to work out the approximate bond energy of an H—Cl bond.

Figure 2

Bond	Bond energy (kJ mol⁻¹)
C — H	413
C — C	347
C — Cl	339
Cl — Cl	239

Bond energy = ... kJ mol⁻¹

[3]

c) Use your answer from b) to rank the bonds from **Figure 2**,
and the H—Cl bond in order of strength, from weakest to strongest.

....

[1]

[Total 5 marks]

Exam Practice Tip

In questions involving calculating energy changes from bond energies (or vice versa), it can be really useful to draw out the <u>displayed formulas</u> of the chemicals that you're dealing with (unless you're given them in the question of course). Displayed formulas show all of the atoms in a molecule and all the bonds between them, so doing this makes it much easier to see what bonds have broken and what new bonds have been made during a chemical reaction.

Fractional Distillation and Hydrocarbons

Warm-Up

Draw a line to match each of the following fractions of crude oil with one of its main uses.

Bitumen		Fuel for aircraft

Diesel		Surfacing roads and roofs

Kerosene		Fuel for cars and trains.

1 Crude oil is a complex mixture of hydrocarbons. *Grade 4-6*

a) What is a hydrocarbon?

....

[2]

b) To which homologous series do most of the hydrocarbons in crude oil belong? Tick **one** box.

☐ **A** alkenes

☐ **B** alkanes

☐ **C** alcohols

☐ **D** carboxylic acids

[1]

c) Crude oil is a finite resource. What does this mean?

....

[1]

[Total 4 marks]

2 The hydrocarbons in crude oil belong to several different homologous series. Compounds in a homologous series all share the same general formula. Give **three** other characteristics of the compounds in a homologous series. *Grade 6-7*

....

....

....

....

....

[Total 3 marks]

3 Propane, C_3H_8, is a hydrocarbon present in the gas fraction of crude oil. **Grade 6-7**

a) Propane can be used as a fuel by burning it in oxygen.

i) Why do hydrocarbons make good fuels?

....

[1]

ii) Write a balanced symbol equation for the complete combustion of propane.

....

[2]

b) Propane is a very small hydrocarbon molecule. Which of the
following statements about propane is **true**? Tick **one** box.

☐ **A** It has a low boiling point and is hard to ignite.

☐ **B** It has a high boiling point and is easy to ignite.

☐ **C** It has a low boiling point and is easy to ignite.

☐ **D** It has a high boiling point and is hard to ignite.

[1]

[Total 4 marks]

4 Kerosene, diesel oil and fuel oil are all fractions of crude oil that
can be used as fuels. The average chain length of the hydrocarbons in
kerosene is shorter than those in diesel oil. The average chain length of
the hydrocarbons in diesel oil is shorter than those in fuel oil. **Grade 6-7**

a) State which of the three fractions named above has the highest boiling point.
Explain your answer with reference to the information above.

....

....

[2]

b) Compare the viscosity of kerosene and fuel oil.
Explain your answer with reference to the information above.

....

....

[2]

c) Compare the ease of ignition of kerosene and diesel oil.
Explain your answer with reference to the information above.

....

....

[2]

[Total 6 marks]

Section 16 — Fuels and Earth Science

5 Crude oil can be separated using the process of fractional distillation. The length of the hydrocarbon chains is fundamental to this process.

Figure 1 shows the boiling points of two molecules that are present in two of the fractions produced by the fractional distillation of crude oil.

Hydrocarbon	Chemical formula	Boiling point (°C)
Heptane	C_7H_{16}	98
Triacontane	$C_{30}H_{62}$	450

Figure 1

a) Triacontane is present in the fuel oil fraction. Give **two** uses of fuel oil.

....

....

[2]

b) i) Which of these two hydrocarbons would you expect to be collected **further down** the fractionating column?

....

[1]

ii) Explain your answer, with reference to the intermolecular forces present between the hydrocarbon molecules.

....

....

....

....

....

....

....

....

[5]

c) A scientist tests the viscosity of heptane, triacontane and a third alkane, alkane **X**. She finds that alkane **X** is more viscous than both heptane and triacontane. Suggest which fraction of crude oil alkane **X** is likely to have been taken from.

....

[1]

[Total 9 marks]

Exam Practice Tip

Remember that if you're given one physical property of a hydrocarbon, you can use it to predict other properties of that compound. For example, if you're told that a certain hydrocarbon has a low boiling point, you can predict that it will have low viscosity, be easy to ignite, and come from a fraction that is collected towards the top of the fractionating column.

Section 16 — Fuels and Earth Science

Pollutants

1   Acid raid is formed when certain gases dissolve in rainwater to form a dilute acid.   **Grade 4-6**

   a) Which of the following gases contributes to acid rain? Tick **one** box.

   ☐ **A** carbon dioxide

   ☐ **B** methane

   ☐ **C** sulfur dioxide

   ☐ **D** carbon monoxide

   [1]

   b) Give **two** possible negative effects of acid rain.

   ....

   ....
   [2]

   [Total 3 marks]

2   Combustion of fuels, such as petrol, in cars is a major contributor to air pollution.   **Grade 6-7**

   a) Explain how cars produce nitrogen oxides.

   ....

   ....
   [2]

   b) Fuel combustion can produce soot. What impact can soot have on human health?

   ....
   [1]

   c) State which toxic gas is produced by incomplete fuel combustion and explain why it is toxic.

   ....

   ....

   ....
   [3]

   d) Hydrogen gas can also be used as a fuel in cars. Give **two** advantages of
   using hydrogen gas rather than fossil fuels as a means of powering vehicles.

   ....

   ....

   ....
   [2]

   [Total 8 marks]

Section 16 — Fuels and Earth Science

Cracking

1 Some hydrocarbons from crude oil undergo processing by the petrochemical industry. For instance, decane, $C_{10}H_{22}$, can undergo cracking as shown in the following equation:

$$C_{10}H_{22} \rightarrow C_8H_{18} + C_2H_4$$

a) C_2H_4 is an unsaturated hydrocarbon. To which homologous series does it belong? Tick **one** box.

☐ **A** alkanes ☐ **B** alkenes ☐ **C** alcohols ☐ **D** carboxylic acids

[1]

b) Explain why a petrochemical company may need to crack hydrocarbons.

....

....

[2]

c) Cracking can form a variety of products.
Write an alternative balanced equation for the cracking of decane.

....

[1]

[Total 4 marks]

2 The hydrocarbon fractions produced by the fractional distillation of crude oil are used in many industrial processes. **Figure 1** shows the approximate percentage of each fraction produced by an oil refinery and the demand for each fraction.

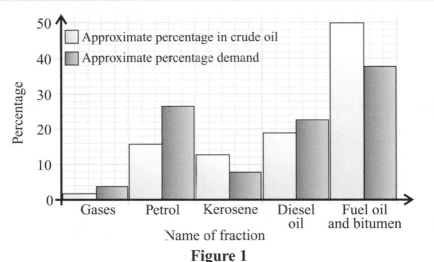

Figure 1

a) The demand for diesel oil is greater than the supply. Using **Figure 1**, name **two** other fractions whose demand is greater than their supply.

....

[2]

b) Suggest what could be done to help match the supply of diesel oil to the demand.

....

....

[1]

[Total 3 marks]

Section 16 — Fuels and Earth Science

The Atmosphere

1 Which of these statements about Earths's early atmosphere is **correct**? Tick **one** box. (Grade 4-6)

☐ **A** The gases that made up Earth's early atmosphere were released by volcanic eruptions.

☐ **B** The Earth's oceans were formed when the methane in the early atmosphere condensed.

☐ **C** Earth's early atmosphere contained less carbon dioxide than the atmosphere today.

☐ **D** Earth's early atmosphere contained a lot of oxygen.

[Total 1 mark]

2 Scientists have looked at the compositions of the atmospheres of other planets to provide evidence for what the early atmosphere on Earth was like. **Figure 1** shows the current compositions of the atmospheres on Mars and Earth. (Grade 6-7)

	Percentage composition (%)					
	H_2O	Ne	CO_2	N_2	O_2	Ar
Mars	0.030	trace	95	2.7	0.13	1.6
Earth	0–4.0	0.0018	0.036	78	21	0.93

Figure 1

a) i) Scientists believe Earth's early atmosphere was similar to the atmosphere on Mars. Using **Figure 1**, suggest which gas made up the majority of Earth's early atmosphere.

....

[1]

ii) Explain **two** ways in which this gas was removed from Earth's atmosphere as it evolved.

....

....

[2]

b) i) Explain how oxygen built up in Earth's atmosphere and suggest why there is hardly any oxygen present in the atmosphere of Mars.

....

....

....

[2]

ii) Describe the chemical test for oxygen.

....

[1]

[Total 6 marks]

The Greenhouse Effect and Climate Change

Identify the statements below that describe things that a family can
do to reduce their carbon dioxide emissions. Tick **two** boxes.

Leaving lights on all day	☐	Using a tumble drier	☐
Walking to school	☐	Turning central heating down	☐
Leaving appliances on standby	☐	Using air conditioning	☐

1 The Earth's atmosphere contains greenhouse gases
which contribute to the greenhouse effect. *(Grade 4-6)*

a) Name **two** greenhouse gases.

....

[2]

b) Give **two** examples of types of human activity which are leading to an
increase in the concentration of greenhouse gases in the atmosphere.

....

....

[2]

[Total 4 marks]

2 The Earth absorbs some electromagnetic radiation from the sun. It then radiates
some of the radiation it absorbs as infrared (IR) radiation. IR radiation
contributes to the greenhouse effect by interacting with greenhouse gases. *(Grade 6-7)*

a) Which of the following statements is **true**? Tick **one** box.

☐ **A** Greenhouse gases absorb all of the IR radiation that is radiated by Earth.

☐ **B** The greenhouse effect is caused by the absorption and
reflection of IR radiation by greenhouse gases.

☐ **C** In general, the higher the concentration of greenhouse gases
in the Earth's atmosphere, the colder the Earth becomes.

☐ **D** Greenhouse gases make up a large percentage of Earth's current atmosphere.

[1]

b) Elvis says he thinks that any amount of any greenhouse gases in the Earth's atmosphere
is dangerous, as it could cause global warming. Is Elvis correct? Explain your answer.

....

....

[1]

[Total 2 marks]

3 Some scientists believe that the increased burning of fossil fuels has contributed to global warming and this has caused glaciers to melt, resulting in rising sea levels. Other scientists believe that the rises in global temperature are just natural fluctuations.

Figure 1 shows CO_2 emissions by fossil fuels in the UK and Crown dependencies and the changes in sea levels between 1993 and 2013.

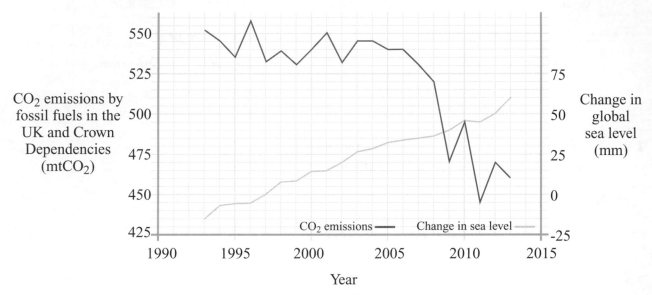

Figure 1

a)* Look at **Figure 1**. Explain whether the data shown on this graph supports a link between human activity and climate change. Discuss any problems associated with using this data to draw conclusions about the affect of carbon dioxide emissions on global sea levels.

....

....

....

....

....

....

....

....

[6]

b) Many governments are trying to decrease their country's CO_2 emissions.
Give **two** ways that the government in the UK is trying to reduce carbon dioxide emissions.

....

....

[2]

[Total 8 marks]

Exam Practice Tip

You could be given data that shows a link between human activity and global warming. But, just because there might be a correlation, it doesn't necessarily mean that one causes the other. You need to evaluate what the data actually shows without making assumptions. For example, if you're given data for one country, you can't assume it's had a global effect.

Section 16 — Fuels and Earth Science

Distance, Displacement, Speed and Velocity

Warm-Up

Write each word below in the table on the right to show whether it is a scalar or vector quantity.

acceleration   time   temperature

mass   weight   force

Scalar	Vector
mass	acceleration
temp	force
time ✓	weight

1   Which of the following correctly defines a vector?   (Grade 4-6)

☐   **A**   Vector quantities only have magnitude.

☐   **B**   Vector quantities show direction but not magnitude.

☒   **C**   Vector quantities have both magnitude and direction.

☐   **D**   Vector quantities are a push or pull on an object.

[Total 1 mark]

2   The speed of sound varies depending upon the substance it is travelling through. State the speed of sound in air.   (Grade 4-6)

.... mach 1 ....

[Total 1 mark]

3   **Figure 1** shows the path taken by a football kicked by a child. When it is kicked at point A, the ball moves horizontally to the right until it hits a vertical wall at Point B. The ball then bounces back horizontally to the left and comes to rest at Point C.   (Grade 4-6)

Figure 1

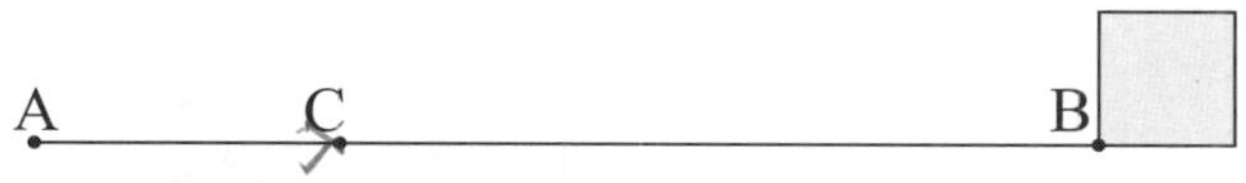

Scale 1 cm = 1 m

A   C   B

a)   Determine the distance that the ball has moved through from A to B.

Distance = ...7.2........... m

[1]

b)   Determine the total distance that the ball has moved through from A to C.

Distance = ...+ 2........... m

[1]

c)   Draw a vector arrow on **Figure 1** to show the displacement of the ball.

[1]

d)   Determine the magnitude of the displacement of the ball after it has come to rest.

Magnitude of displacement = ...2........... m

[1]

[Total 4 marks]

162

4 A student went for a run. She ran for exactly 22 minutes at an average speed of 4.0 m/s.

a) State the equation that links distance travelled, average speed and time.

$s = \frac{d}{t}$

....

[1]

b) Calculate the distance that the student ran in km. Give your answer to two significant figures.

$4 \times 1320 = 5280\text{m}$

$22 \times 60 = 1320$

Distance = ...5.28........ km

[4]

[Total 5 marks]

5 A journalist is deciding whether to walk, cycle or take a bus to get to work. There are two routes he could take. The shorter route is along a 3.5 km path that only pedestrians and cyclists are allowed to use. The bus takes a longer route along a road.

a) Estimate how long it would take the journalist to walk the pedestrian route.

$\frac{3500}{1.5} = 2333\text{s}$

1.5x

Time taken = ...2333........ s

[4]

b) Estimate how much time would be saved if the journalist were to cycle this route instead.

$2333 - 233 = 2100$

$\frac{3500}{15} = 233$

Time saved = ...2100........ s

[4]

c) Travelling to work by bus takes 15 minutes.
The total distance covered during this time is 7.2 km.
Calculate the average speed of the bus in m/s.

15×60

$\frac{7200}{900} = 8$

Speed = ...8........ m/s

[3]

[Total 11 marks]

Acceleration

Draw one line from each scenario on the left to the typical acceleration for that object.

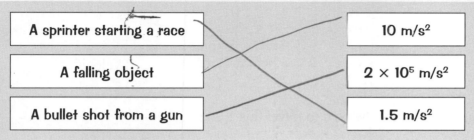

A sprinter starting a race		10 m/s²
A falling object		2 × 10⁵ m/s²
A bullet shot from a gun		1.5 m/s²

1 Describe the motion of an object that has a negative acceleration.

it is going backwards or slowing down

[Total 1 mark]

2 A dog sets off from rest and reaches a speed of 3.2 m/s in 8.0 s.

a) Calculate the dog's average acceleration.

$$\frac{3.2^2}{8} = 1.28$$

Acceleration = ...1.28..... m/s²

[3]

b) The dog keeps running with this acceleration for a further 6.0 s. Calculate the dog's final speed.

Speed = ...1.co.,88... m/s

[3]

[Total 6 marks]

3 A pebble is dropped from a height level with the end of a diving board above a lake. The velocity of the pebble immediately before it hits the surface of the water is 12 m/s.

Calculate the height of the diving board.

$$\frac{v^2 - u^2}{2 \times a \times x} \qquad \frac{12^2 - 0}{2 \times 10} = 7.2$$

Height = ...7.2..... m

[Total 3 marks]

Section 17 — Motion, Forces and Conservation of Energy

4 A boat is travelling at a constant velocity of 5.0 m/s. It then starts to accelerate with a constant acceleration of 0.25 m/s² for a distance of 1.2 km.

a) Calculate the final velocity of the boat.

$$2 \times 0.25 \times 1200 + 5 = 605$$

Velocity = ...605........ m/s

[3]

b) Calculate the time it takes for the boat to travel this 1.2 km.

$$\frac{605 + 5}{0.25} = 2400$$

Time = ...2400....... s

[3]

[Total 6 marks]

5 A train travelling at 30 m/s slows down to 18 m/s over a distance of 360 m. Calculate the average deceleration of the train over this distance.

$$\frac{18 - 30}{360} = 2a$$

$$a = \frac{2a}{2} = -0.6$$

Deceleration = ...-0.06........ m/s²

[Total 3 marks]

6 A cyclist is travelling along a main road. The cyclist stops at a red light. When the light changes to green, the cyclist accelerates with a uniform acceleration up to a speed of 21 km/hr. Estimate the cyclist's acceleration in m/s².

$$21 \times 1000 = 21000$$

$$21000 \times 600 = 12600000$$

$$\frac{1260000^2 - 0}{125} = 126000000000000$$

Acceleration = ... m/s²

[Total 3 marks]

Exam Practice Tip

Watch out for questions on acceleration — if you aren't given an equation in the question, you'll have to decide which acceleration equation you need to use. Making a list of the information you have can help, and look out for key words — 'uniform', 'constant', 'increasing' or 'decreasing' might give you a clue as to which equation to use.

Distance/Time Graphs

1   A boat is being rowed along a straight canal. Some students time how long after setting off the boat passes marker posts spaced 100 metres apart. **Figure 1** shows their results.

Figure 1

Distance (m)	0	100	200	300	400	500
Time (s)	0	85	165	250	335	420

Figure 2

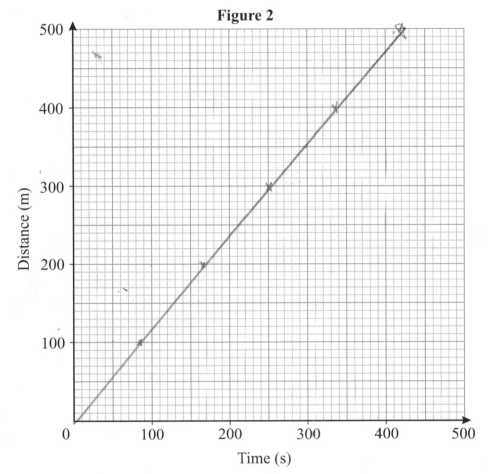

a)   Draw the distance/time graph for the results in **Figure 1** on the axes shown in **Figure 2**.

[3]

b)   Using **Figure 2**, determine how far the boat travelled in 300 s.

Distance = 350 m

[1]

c)   Determine the time taken for the boat to travel 250 m, using **Figure 2**.

Time = 210 s

[1]

d)   The students take the timings using a stopwatch. Suggest **one** way the students can make their measurements are as accurate as possible.

using a light gate or video recording

[1]

[Total 6 marks]

Section 17 — Motion, Forces and Conservation of Energy

2   **Figure 3** shows the distance/time graph for a cyclist's bike ride.

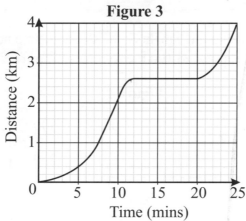

Figure 3

a) Determine how long the cyclist rode for before stopping for a rest.

2 .6 km

[1]

b) Describe the cyclist's motion in the first five minutes of her journey.

exponential

[1]

[Total 2 marks]

3   **Figure 4** shows the distance/time graph for a car's journey.

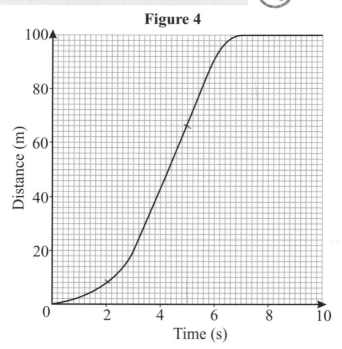

Figure 4

a) Use **Figure 4** to find the speed of the car 5 s into its journey.

$\frac{66}{5} = 13.2$

Speed = ...13.2....... m/s

[3]

b) Use **Figure 4** to find the speed of the car 2 s into its journey.

$\frac{8}{2} = 4$

Speed = ...4......... m/s

[3]

[Total 6 marks]

Section 17 — Motion, Forces and Conservation of Energy

Velocity/Time Graphs

Warm-Up

Use two of the phrases from the list below to correctly label the velocity/time graph.

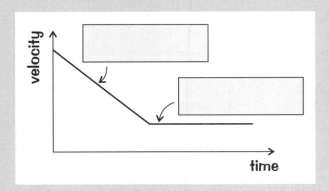

decreasing deceleration

steady speed

decreasing acceleration

constant acceleration

constant deceleration

1 Velocity/time graphs can be used to show the motion of an object.

Which quantity is represented by the area under a velocity/time graph?

- ☐ **A** speed
- ☐ **B** acceleration
- ☒ **C** distance
- ☐ **D** deceleration

[Total 1 mark]

2 A bear runs with a constant acceleration for 10 s before running at a constant velocity of 8 m/s for a further 10 s. Which of the following velocity/time graphs shows this?

☒ **A**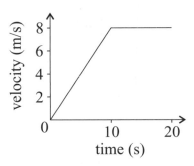

☐ **B**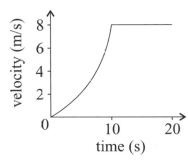

☐ **C**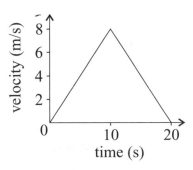

☐ **D**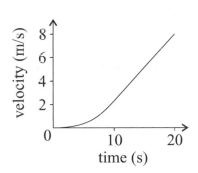

[Total 1 mark]

Section 17 — Motion, Forces and Conservation of Energy

3 **Figure 1** shows an incomplete velocity/time graph for a rollercoaster ride.

Figure 1

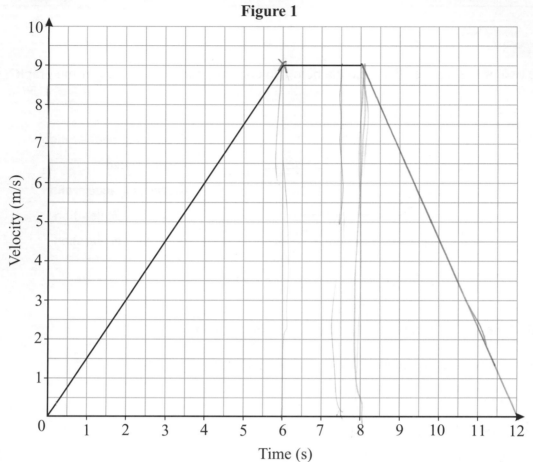

a) After 8 seconds, the rollercoaster decelerates at an increasing rate.
   It comes to rest 4 seconds after it begins decelerating.
   Complete the velocity/time graph in **Figure 1** to show this.

[2]

b) Calculate the acceleration of the rollercoaster during the first 6 seconds of the ride.

$\frac{9}{6} = 1.5$

Acceleration = ...1.5.......... m/s²
[2]

c) Calculate the distance travelled by the rollercoaster between 0 and 8 s.

$6 \times 9 = \frac{54}{2} = 27$

$1.5 \times 9 = 13.5$

$\Big\} +2 = 40.5$

Distance = ...60.5.......... m
[3]

d) Estimate the distance travelled by the rollercoaster between 8 and 12 seconds,
   to the nearest metre.

$9 \times 4 = 36$

$\frac{}{2} = 18$

Distance = ...18.......... m
[3]

[Total 10 marks]

Section 17 — Motion, Forces and Conservation of Energy

Newton's First and Second Laws

Use the words and phrases below to correctly fill in the gaps in the passage. You don't have to use all of them, but each one can only be used once.

Newton's ......*First*...... Law of motion says that an object will remain stationary or

moving at ......*a constant velocity*...... if there is ......*a zero*...... resultant force acting on it.

If there is ......*a non-zero*...... resultant force acting on the object, it will ......*accelerate*...... .

a constant velocity	accelerate	a zero	First
a non-zero	Second	remain stationary	an increasing speed

---

1 A rocket moves at a constant speed in space. In order to change its speed, it turns on its thrusters, accelerates to the desired speed and then turns them off again.

a) The mass of the rocket is 110 000 kg and it accelerates at 5.0 m/s². What is the force provided by the thrusters?

☒ **A** 550 000 N

☐ **B** 55 000 N

☐ **C** 22 000 N

☐ **D** 220 000 N

[1]

b) State why the rocket continues moving at a constant speed after turning off its thrusters.

......*because there is no force acting on the rocket*......

......

[1]

[Total 2 marks]

---

2 A vase is knocked from a shelf. As the vase begins to fall, the resultant force acting on it is 38 N. Acceleration due to gravity is 10 m/s². Calculate the mass of the vase.

$$\frac{38}{10} = 3.8$$

Mass = ...*3.8*...... kg

[Total 3 marks]

---

3 A sailboat has a mass of 60 kg and is accelerating at 0.4 m/s^2. The wind acting on the sail provides a force of 44 N. The drag from the water acts in the opposite direction.

Calculate the force of the drag acting on the boat. Show your working.

Force = ...15..... N

[Total 4 marks]

4 A car is travelling at 14 m/s when it hits a wall. It experiences a large, constant deceleration and quickly comes to a stop.

a) Explain why very large decelerations can be dangerous.

....

....

[2]

b) Estimate the size of the resultant force acting on the car during the collision.

Force = ... N

[5]

[Total 7 marks]

5 **Figure 1** shows a 7520 kg lorry. The driver spots a hazard ahead and applies the brakes. The lorry decelerates uniformly and comes to a stop 50 m after the brakes are applied. Estimate the braking force needed to stop the lorry.

Figure 1

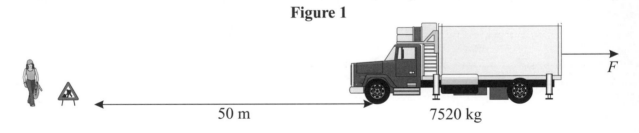

50 m   7520 kg

Force = ... N

[Total 5 marks]

Exam Practice Tip

Watch out for questions talking about constant or uniform acceleration over a distance. They can be tricky with lots of steps. In the exam, use the equation from the equation sheet that links velocity, acceleration and distance to find the acceleration (or deceleration) of an object. Then stick it into Newton's 2nd Law to find the resultant force on the object.

Section 17 — Motion, Forces and Conservation of Energy

Weight and Circular Motion

Warm-Up

State whether each of the following statements are true or false.

1) The acceleration of an object in free fall on Earth is 10 m/s². _____

2) The weight of an object is the same everywhere. _____

3) The mass of an object is the same everywhere. _____

4) The weight of an object on the moon is smaller than on Earth. _____

1 An astronaut weighs herself on Earth and on the Moon. **Grade 4-6**

a) State what is meant by weight.

....

....
[1]

b) On Earth, the astronaut has a mass of 65 kg. Calculate her weight on Earth.
Use the equation:

$$\text{weight} = \text{mass of object} \times \text{gravitational field strength}$$

Weight = ... N
[2]

c) She wears her spacesuit which has a mass of 80 kg. On the Moon, the astronaut and
the spacesuit have a combined weight 232 N. Calculate the gravitational field strength
of the Moon at its surface.

Gravitational field strength = ... Unit ....
[3]

[Total 6 marks]

2 Does a satellite orbiting the Earth at 3.07 x 10³ m/s have a constant velocity? **Grade 6-7**
Explain your answer.

....

....

....
[Total 2 marks]

Section 17 — Motion, Forces and Conservation of Energy

Investigating Motion

1 A student uses the apparatus in **Figure 1** to investigate the effect of changing the mass of a trolley on its acceleration. The trolley is on a ramp to compensate for friction.

The student records the mass of the trolley and the weight of the hook. The hook has a weight of 1.5 N.

When the hook is allowed to fall, the trolley accelerates. The student then records the time it takes the trolley to travel between the two light gates and the speed of the trolley as it passes through each light gate.

Figure 1

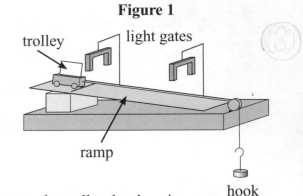

The student repeats this process, each time adding a mass to the trolley, but keeping the hook the same. Every time she adds a mass to the trolley, she changes the height of the ramp so that friction between the ramp and the trolley can be ignored.

a) Give **one** benefit of using light gates to take measurements.

....

....
[1]

b) Describe how the student uses her measurements to determine the acceleration of the trolley.

....

....
[1]

c) i) Calculate the acceleration of the trolley when the total mass of the system is 3 kg.

Acceleration = ... m/s²
[3]

ii) Predict how the acceleration of the trolley will change as the mass of the trolley is increased.

....

....
[1]

d) The student wants to calculate the uncertainty of one of her mean results. Describe how she can do this.

....

....
[2]
[Total 8 marks]

Section 17 — Motion, Forces and Conservation of Energy

Inertia and Newton's Third Law

Which of the following is Newton's Third Law? Tick **one** box.

A non-zero resultant force is needed to cause a change in speed or direction. ☐

A resultant force is inversely proportional to the mass of an object. ☐

When two objects interact, they exert equal and opposite forces on each other. ☐

A resultant force of zero leads to an equilibrium situation. ☐

1   All objects have an inertial mass. (Grade 6-7)

a) State the meaning of the term inertial mass.

....

[1]

Three identical shopping trolleys, A, B and C, are filled with different items and so that each trolley has a different mass. Each trolley is pushed with an equal force from the same starting point, and its velocity is recorded immediately afterwards. **Figure 1** shows the results.

Figure 1

Trolley	A	B	C
Velocity (m/s)	1.5	0.7	2.2

b) State which trolley has the highest inertial mass. Explain your answer.

....

....

[2]

[Total 3 marks]

2   Two students each stand at rest on a skateboard by a wall. They both push against the wall with a force of 24 N. You can assume there is no friction between the skateboards and the ground. (Grade 6-7)

a) Explain in terms of forces why the students would move away from the wall.

....

....

[2]

b) Student A and his skateboard have a combined mass of 80 kg. Student B and his skateboard have a combined mass of 40 kg. What is the difference in their accelerations?

☐ **A** 0.3 m/s²   ☐ **B** 0.6 m/s²

☐ **C** 1.6 m/s²   ☐ **D** 3.3 m/s²

[1]

[Total 3 marks]

Momentum

1 A motorbike is travelling at 25 m/s and has a mass of 220 kg. *(Grade 4-6)*

a) State the equation that links momentum, mass and velocity.

....

[1]

b) Calculate the momentum of the motorbike.

Momentum = ... kg m/s

[2]

[Total 3 marks]

2 A car is moving east with a velocity of 15 m/s and momentum 46 000 kg m/s. *(Grade 4-6)*

Calculate the mass of the car.

Mass = ... kg

[Total 3 marks]

3 **Figure 1** and **Figure 2** show a Newton's cradle. All of the balls on the cradle have the same mass. *(Grade 6-7)*

Figure 1	Figure 2

When a ball is lifted and allowed to hit the others as shown in **Figure 1**, it causes the last ball in the line to move outwards, as shown in **Figure 2**. The balls in between appear to remain stationary. Using conservation of momentum, explain this behaviour.

....

....

....

....

....

....

[Total 4 marks]

Section 17 — Motion, Forces and Conservation of Energy

4 A ball moves with an initial velocity of 3 m/s. It comes to rest after 4 seconds due to a constant resistive force of 0.15 N. Calculate the mass of the ball.

Mass = ... kg

[Total 3 marks]

5 **Figure 3** shows two American football players running towards each other. They collide and cling together in a tackle. Calculate the velocity that they move together with once they have collided.

Figure 3

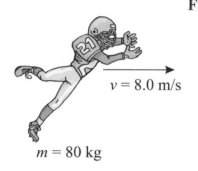 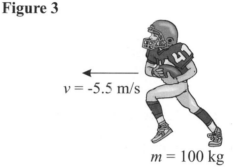

$v = 8.0$ m/s $v = -5.5$ m/s

$m = 80$ kg $m = 100$ kg

Velocity = ... m/s

[Total 4 marks]

6 **Figure 4** shows balls 1 and 2 before and after a collision.

Ball 1 initially travels with a velocity of u m/s. Ball 2 is stationary and has a mass of 0.2 kg. Ball 1 collides with ball 2 and this collision lasts for 0.1 s. Afterwards, both balls move in the direction of ball 1's initial velocity. Each ball has a different final velocity.

Figure 4

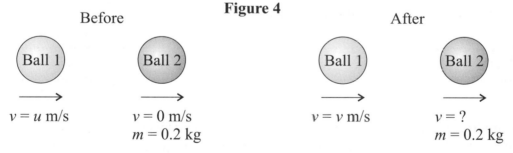

Before   After

Ball 1   Ball 2   Ball 1   Ball 2

$v = u$ m/s $v = 0$ m/s $v = v$ m/s $v = ?$

$m = 0.2$ kg $m = 0.2$ kg

During the collision, a force of –6 N is exerted on ball 1 by ball 2.
Calculate the velocity of ball 2 after the collision.

Velocity = ... m/s

[Total 5 marks]

Section 17 — Motion, Forces and Conservation of Energy

Stopping Distances and Reaction Times

1 The thinking distance for a driver in a car travelling at 40 mph is 12 m. The braking distance is 24 m. *(Grade 4-6)*

a) State what is meant by thinking distance.

....

....
[1]

b) Calculate the car's stopping distance when it is travelling at 40 mph.

Stopping Distance = ... m
[1]

[Total 2 marks]

2 Different people have different reaction times. *(Grade 4-6)*

a) What is the typical reaction time for a person?

☐ **A** 1.3 – 1.8 s   ☐ **B** 0.4 – 0.9 s   ☐ **C** 0.1 – 0.2 s   ☐ **D** 2.0 – 3.0 s
[1]

b) Give **three** factors that could affect a person's reaction time.

....

....
[3]

[Total 4 marks]

3 A car is travelling down a road, and the driver has to brake suddenly. *(Grade 4-6)*

a) Describe what is meant by braking distance.

....

....
[1]

b) There are lots of leaves on the road, and the road surface is wet.
Explain what effect this will have on the car's braking distance.

....

....

....

....
[2]

[Total 3 marks]

4   The ruler drop test can be used to investigate people's reaction times.   (Grade 6-7)

a)   Describe **one** other method that can be used to test people's reaction times.

....

[1]

b)   Describe the steps involved when using the ruler drop experiment to investigate reaction times.

....

....

....

....

....

....

....

....

[6]

[Total 7 marks]

5*   A group of friends are driving home from a concert late at night. It is raining heavily and they are listening to loud music on the radio.   (Grade 6-7)

Describe the factors that could affect the car's stopping distance and safety of the journey. Explain the effect each factor could have.

....

....

....

....

....

....

....

....

....

....

....

[Total 6 marks]

Section 17 — Motion, Forces and Conservation of Energy

Energy Stores

Match each of the following energy stores to the object which mainly has energy in that store.

Kinetic energy store	A nucleus about to undergo a nuclear reaction
Magnetic energy store	A stretched rubber band
Electrostatic energy store	A hot potato
Chemical energy store	A person on top of a mountain
Elastic potential energy store	A toy car rolling along the ground
Nuclear energy store	Two magnets attracted to each other
Thermal energy store	Petrol in a car
Gravitational potential energy store	Two electric charges repelling each other

1   A 0.1 kg toy contains a compressed spring. When the spring
is released, the toy flies 0.5 m upwards from ground level.

Calculate the change in energy stored in the toy's gravitational potential energy store when it
reaches its highest point. The gravitational field strength of Earth is 10 N/kg. Use the equation:

$$\text{change in gravitational potential energy} = \text{mass} \times \text{gravitational field strength} \times \text{change in vertical height}$$

Energy = ... 0.5 .... J

[Total 2 marks]

2   A 0.50 kg rock is dropped from a cliff edge.
It falls 42 m before entering the sea.

a) State the equation that links the energy in an object's kinetic energy store, its mass and its speed.

....

[1]

b) Calculate the speed of the rock when it hits the water.
You can assume there is no air resistance and that all of the energy transferred from the
rock's gravitational potential energy store is transferred to its kinetic energy store.
Gravitational field strength = 10 N/kg.

Speed = ... m/s

[5]

[Total 6 marks]

Section 17 — Motion, Forces and Conservation of Energy

Transferring Energy

Warm-Up

A ball is rolling along the ground. It slows down and eventually stops.
Fill in the blanks in the energy transfer diagram using the words given below.

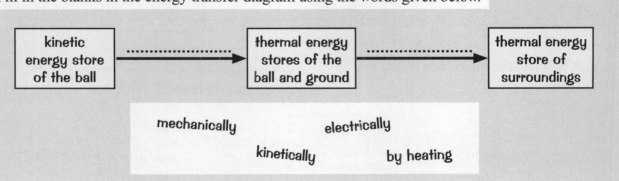

| kinetic energy store of the ball | ·····▶ | thermal energy stores of the ball and ground | ·····▶ | thermal energy store of surroundings |

mechanically   electrically

kinetically   by heating

1   Energy can be transferred between different energy stores.   (Grade 6-7)

a) State the principle of conservation of energy.

....

....

[1]

b) A kettle of cold water is plugged into the mains and brought to the boil.
Describe how is energy transferred from the mains to the kettle.

....

[1]

c) Describe the main energy transfer for a bike freewheeling down a hill.
You should refer to the energy stores that the energy is transferred between in your answer.

....

....

....

[3]

d) Describe the energy transfers for a golf club hitting a ball.
You should refer to the energy stores that the energy is transferred between in your answer.

....

....

....

....

....

[4]

[Total 9 marks]

      Section 17 — Motion, Forces and Conservation of Energy

Efficiency

1 An electric fan transfers 7250 J of energy. 2030 J of this is wasted energy.

   a) Suggest **one** way in which energy is wasted by the fan.

   ....
   [1]

   b) Calculate the efficiency of the fan.

   Efficiency = ...
   [3]
   [Total 4 marks]

2 A student investigates the efficiency of a scale model of an electricity generating wind turbine using the equipment in **Figure 1**. He changes the number of sails on the turbine and calculates the energy transferred by the turbine's generator. The air blower is supplied with 30 kJ of energy and has an efficiency of 0.6.

Figure 1

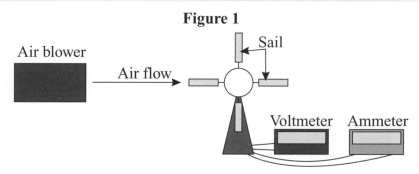

   a) When using two sails, the efficiency of the turbine was 12%.
      Calculate the useful energy transferred out from the turbine.

   Energy transferred = ... J
   [4]

   b) Describe **two** ways the student could increase the efficiency of the turbine.

   1. ....

   2. ....
   [2]
   [Total 6 marks]

Exam Practice Tip

Some of the energy input to a device is always dissipated or wasted. If you're asked to suggest ways to improve the efficiency of a device, think about how energy is wasted and then what could be done to reduce that waste.

Section 17 — Motion, Forces and Conservation of Energy

Reducing Unwanted Energy Transfers

1   A woman is cycling in a race. Before the race, she puts oil on the bike chain.   Grade 4-6

Explain why putting the oil on the bike chain increases the efficiency of the woman's cycling.

....

....

[Total 2 marks]

2   A builder is trying to minimise the rate at which a house cools.   Grade 4-6

a) The builder can build the walls of the house using bricks A-D. Based on the information in the table below, which type of brick should she use?

		Thermal conductivity	Brick width
☐	**A**	High	10 cm
☐	**B**	High	15 cm
☐	**C**	Low	10 cm
☐	**D**	Low	15 cm

[1]

b) Give **one** other way the builder could reduce the rate at which the house cools.

....

[1]

c) **Figure 1** shows the energy transfer diagram for the builder's electric drill.
It shows the energy transferred when it is used for 30 seconds.

Figure 1

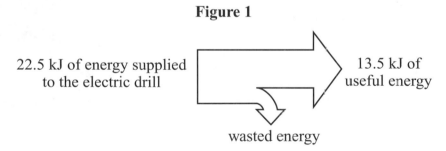

22.5 kJ of energy supplied
to the electric drill

13.5 kJ of
useful energy

wasted energy

Calculate how much energy is wasted during this time.

Wasted energy = ... kJ

[1]

[Total 3 marks]

 ☐   ☐   ☐

Energy Resources

Write the energy resources below in the correct column to show whether they are renewable or non-renewable.

bio-fuel   hydro-electricity

coal

solar

wind   nuclear fuel

tidal

oil   gas

Renewable	Non-renewable

---

1   Describe the difference between renewable and non-renewable energy resources.   (Grade 4-6)

....

....

[Total 2 marks]

---

2   Most cars, like the one in **Figure 1**, run on petrol or diesel, which are both derived from fossil fuels.   (Grade 4-6)

Figure 1

a)   Name the **three** fossil fuels.

....

[1]

b)   Give **one** other everyday use for fossil fuels.

....

[1]

c)   Some modern cars are made to run on bio-fuels. State what is meant by bio-fuels.

....

....

[1]

d)   Suggest **one** reason why car manufacturers are developing cars that run on alternative fuels to petrol and diesel.

....

....

[1]

[Total 4 marks]

3 A university is considering ways to reduce their energy bills. They are considering building either a single wind turbine nearby, or installing solar panels on top of their buildings. *Grade 6-7*

a) Suggest **two** reasons why students living near the turbine may prefer the use of solar power.

1. ....

2. ....

[2]

b) Suggest **one** reason why the university may choose a wind turbine over solar panels.

....

[1]

[Total 3 marks]

4 An energy provider is looking to replace their old fossil fuel power plant. They are eligible for a government grant, so the initial building costs are negligible. *Grade 7-9*

a) The energy provider is interested in building a power plant that uses renewable energy resources. They have narrowed their choice to either a hydro-electric power plant or a tidal barrage. Compare generating electricity using these two energy resources, commenting on their reliability and their impact on the environment.

....

....

....

....

....

....

....

....

[5]

b)* An alternative is replacing the old power plant with a new power plant that is run on fossil fuels. Discuss the advantages and disadvantages of using fossil fuels to generate electricity.

....

....

....

....

....

....

....

....

[6]

[Total 11 marks]

Section 17 — Motion, Forces and Conservation of Energy

Trends in Energy Resource Use

1 The bar chart in **Figure 1** below shows the electricity generated from renewable and non-renewable energy sources in a small country over 20 years.

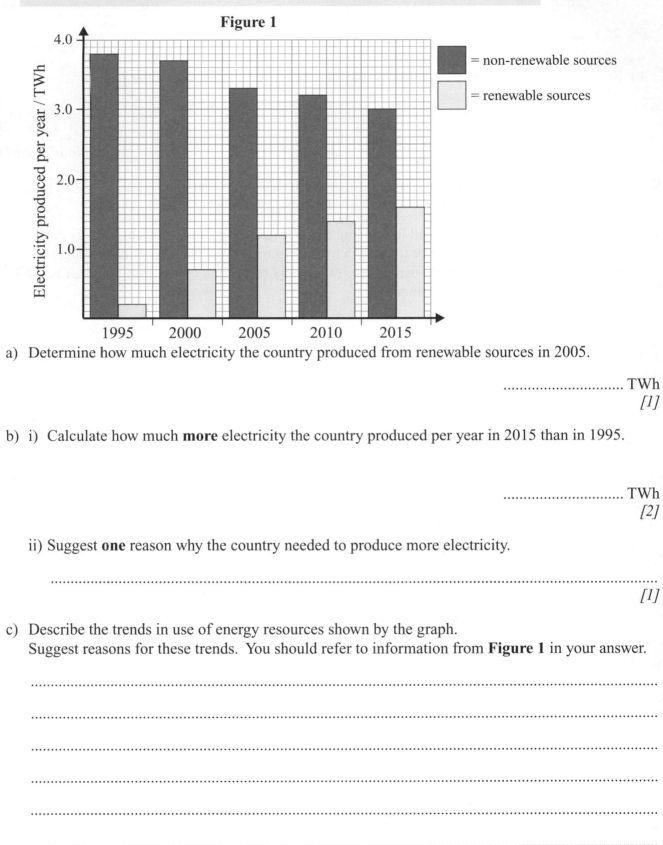

Figure 1

a) Determine how much electricity the country produced from renewable sources in 2005.

.... TWh

[1]

b) i) Calculate how much **more** electricity the country produced per year in 2015 than in 1995.

.... TWh

[2]

ii) Suggest **one** reason why the country needed to produce more electricity.

....

[1]

c) Describe the trends in use of energy resources shown by the graph.
Suggest reasons for these trends. You should refer to information from **Figure 1** in your answer.

....

....

....

....

....

....

....

[4]

[Total 8 marks]

Section 17 — Motion, Forces and Conservation of Energy

Wave Basics

Warm-Up

Add the labels below to the diagram of the wave.

amplitude   crest

rest position

wavelength   trough

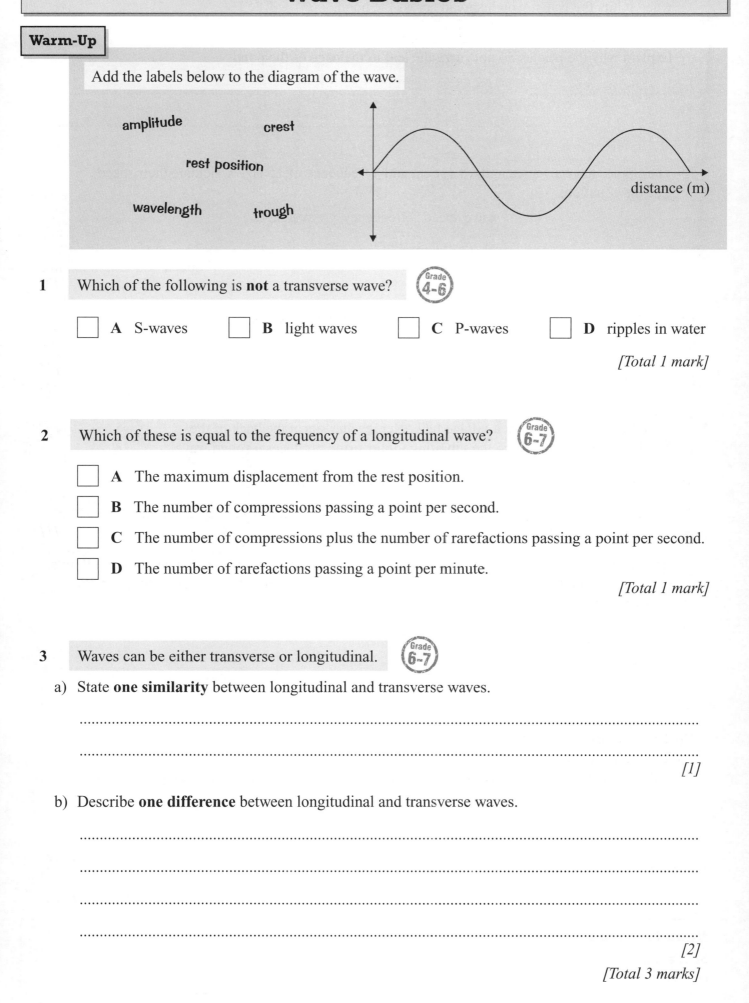

distance (m)

---

1 Which of the following is **not** a transverse wave? *Grade 4-6*

☐ **A** S-waves   ☐ **B** light waves   ☐ **C** P-waves   ☐ **D** ripples in water

[Total 1 mark]

---

2 Which of these is equal to the frequency of a longitudinal wave? *Grade 6-7*

☐ **A** The maximum displacement from the rest position.

☐ **B** The number of compressions passing a point per second.

☐ **C** The number of compressions plus the number of rarefactions passing a point per second.

☐ **D** The number of rarefactions passing a point per minute.

[Total 1 mark]

---

3 Waves can be either transverse or longitudinal. *Grade 6-7*

a) State **one similarity** between longitudinal and transverse waves.

....

....

[1]

b) Describe **one difference** between longitudinal and transverse waves.

....

....

....

....

[2]

[Total 3 marks]

4 A child throws a stone into a pond. The stone creates ripples when it hits the water, which spread across the pond.

Grade 6-7

a) The ripples pass a leaf floating on the pond.
Explain why the ripples do not carry the leaf to the edge of the pond.

....

....

[1]

b) The ripples have a wavelength of 1.4 cm and a frequency of 15 Hz. Calculate their speed.
Use the equation:

wave speed = frequency × wavelength

Speed = ... m/s
[2]

c) The ripples have a period of 0.25 s. Explain what is meant by the period of a wave.

....

[1]

[Total 4 marks]

5 A violinist is practising in a village hall. Her teacher sits at the back of the hall to listen. As she plays, the vibrating violin string produces a sound wave.

Grade 6-7

a) i) State the equation that links wave speed, distance and time.

....

[1]

ii) The violinist's teacher sits 17 m away from her. The sound waves travel at a speed of 340 m/s. Calculate the time taken for the teacher to hear the sound produced by the violin when the student begins playing.

Time = ... s
[2]

b) The violinist then plays a note with a frequency of 220 Hz.
The violinist plays this note for 5.0 seconds.
Calculate how many complete sound waves are produced by the vibrating string in this time.

.... waves
[2]

[Total 5 marks]

Exam Practice Tip

Be careful with units when you're working with waves. You need to remember to convert everything into the right units before you do any calculations, or your answers will come out either too big or too small, and you won't get full marks.

Section 18 — Waves and the Electromagnetic Spectrum

Measuring Waves

1   The wave speed in a solid can be found by hitting a metal rod with a
    hammer, shown in **Figure 1**. The sound waves produced when the rod
    is struck are recorded by the microphone and displayed by a computer.

Figure 1

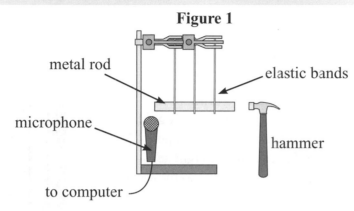

metal rod

elastic bands

microphone

hammer

to computer

A 20 cm metal rod is hit by the hammer. The peak frequency produced was 8500 Hz.
Calculate the speed of the wave produced in the rod.

Speed = ... m/s

[Total 4 marks]

2   A student uses the equipment shown in **Figure 2** to investigate water waves in a ripple tank.

Figure 2

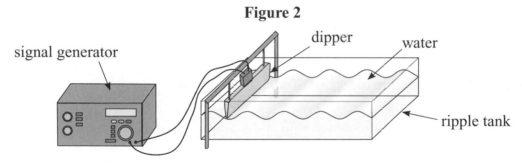

signal generator

dipper

water

ripple tank

a) The student wants to measure the frequency of the ripples. She floats a cork in the ripple
    tank, and counts how many times it bobs up in 30 seconds. The student repeats her
    experiment five times. She does not adjust the signal generator between repeats.

    State **two** other factors that should remain the same between repeats.

    ....

    ....

    [2]

Figure 3 shows the student's results. She recorded one of the results incorrectly.

Figure 3

trial	1	2	3	4	5
number of bobs in 30 seconds	12	11	21	11	14

b) i) Calculate the average number of times the cork bobbed up in 30 seconds, ignoring the anomalous result.

Average number of bobs = ...
[3]

ii) Using your answer to part i), calculate the average frequency of the ripples.

Frequency = ... Hz
[2]

Figure 4

18 cm

c) The student then decides to adjust her experiment to investigate the speed of the ripples. She sets the signal generator to 12 Hz. She then places a piece of paper underneath the ripple tank and uses a strobe light set to the same frequency as the signal generator so the waves appear to not move.

Figure 4 shows the wave pattern produced on the paper.

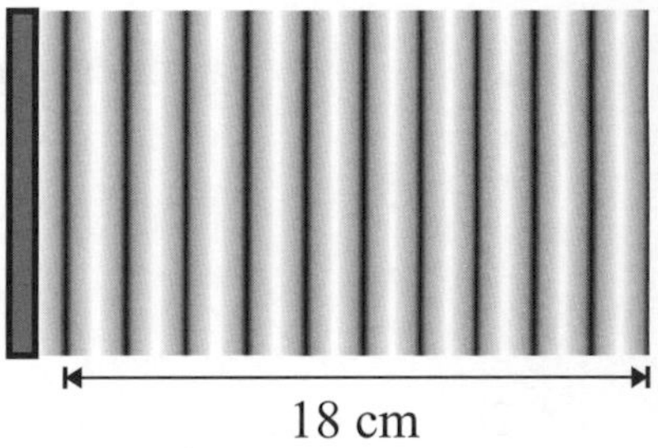

i) Write down the equation that links wave speed, frequency and wavelength.

....
[1]

ii) Calculate the speed of the water ripples.
Give your answer to an appropriate number of significant figures.

Speed = ... m/s
[3]

[Total 11 marks]

3* Describe a method to measure the speed of sound waves in air. (Grade 7-9)

....

....

....

....

....

....

....

....

....

....

....

....

[Total 6 marks]

Wave Behaviour at Boundaries

At the boundary with a new material, a wave can be reflected, absorbed or transmitted. Draw a line to match each option to the description which best matches it.

wave is reflected	it passes through the material
wave is absorbed	it bounces back off the material
wave is transmitted	it transfers all its energy to the material

1 In each of the following situations, a wave encounters a boundary between two materials. Describe the effects you would expect to see for the following wave behaviours.

a) A sound wave reflecting off a hard, flat surface.

....

[1]

b) A ray of visible light being absorbed by a black object.

....

[1]

[Total 2 marks]

2 **Figure 1** shows a ray of light travelling from air into a clear, rectangular block of an unknown material.

Figure 1

Air   Block of clear material

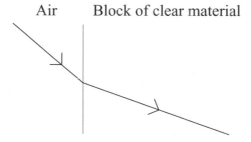

a) What is the angle of incidence for the light ray entering the block? Use a protractor to accurately measure the angle.

Angle of incidence = ... °

[1]

b) State and explain **one** conclusion you can make about the material of the block, compared to air.

....

....

[2]

[Total 3 marks]

Section 18 — Waves and the Electromagnetic Spectrum

Investigating Refraction

1   A student is investigating refraction through different materials. The student uses a
ray box to shine a ray of light into blocks of materials at a fixed angle of incidence,
I. He traces the path of the ray entering and leaving the block on a sheet of paper.

a) Explain why a ray box was used for this experiment.

....

....

[1]

Figure 1

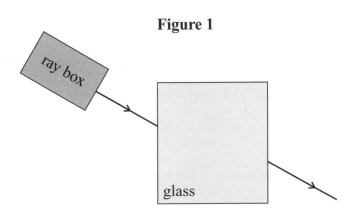

b) **Figure 1** shows the student's investigation for light refracted through a glass block.
Complete the diagram by drawing the light ray as it passes through the glass block.

[1]

c) The student measures the angle of refraction, *R*, of the light ray as it enters the block.
Figure 2 shows the results for a range of materials. Complete **Figure 2** by measuring
the angle of refraction for the glass block shown in **Figure 1**.

Figure 2

Material	*I*	*R*
Cooking Oil	30°	20°
Water	30°	22°
Plastic	30°	20°
Glass	30°	....

[1]

d) State and explain which of the materials shown in **Figure 2** changes the speed of the light ray
the least.

....

....

....

[3]

[Total 6 marks]

Electromagnetic Waves

Warm-Up

For each sentence, circle whether it is true or false.

All electromagnetic waves are transverse. **True / False**

All electromagnetic waves travel at the same speed in a vacuum. **True / False**

Human eyes can detect a large part of the electromagnetic spectrum. **True / False**

---

1 **Figure 1** is an incomplete table describing the energies of different types of radiation in the electromagnetic spectrum.

Figure 1

Low Energy						High Energy
Radio Waves	Microwaves	....	Visible Light	Ultraviolet	....	Gamma Rays

a) Complete **Figure 1** by filling in the missing types of electromagnetic radiation.

[2]

b) Draw an arrow beneath **Figure 1** that points from the type of electromagnetic radiation with the shortest wavelength towards the type with the longest wavelength.

[1]

c) The visible light section of the electromagnetic spectrum can be split further into the bands of wavelengths that make up each colour. Complete the list in **Figure 2**, which lists the colours of visible light in terms of increasing wavelength.

Figure 2

Red, Orange, ... , ... , ... , ... , Violet

[2]

d) Electromagnetic waves can be generated by changes within atoms.
State which part of the atom can generate gamma rays.

....

[1]

[Total 7 marks]

2 Some types of electromagnetic wave can be harmful to people.

a) Describe how the potential danger an electromagnetic wave poses to a person varies with its frequency.

....

[1]

Section 18 — Waves and the Electromagnetic Spectrum

b) Draw lines to match the types of electromagnetic radiation on the left to their potential side effects on the right.

Infrared	internal heating of cells
Microwaves	skin burns
X-rays	cell mutation and cancer

[1]

c) Another type of harmful electromagnetic radiation is ultraviolet radiation. Give **two** damaging effects of ultraviolet light.

1. ....

2. ....

[2]

[Total 4 marks]

3 X-rays are used in hospitals to diagnose broken bones. (Grade 6-7)

The X-rays are generated by accelerating electrons to high speeds then firing them at a metal plate. When the electrons hit the plate, X-rays are produced.

Staff who work with X-ray machines wear badges that monitor the levels of radiation they have been exposed to, shown in **Figure 3**. These badges contain a photographic film which undergoes a chemical change when exposed to X-rays.

Figure 3

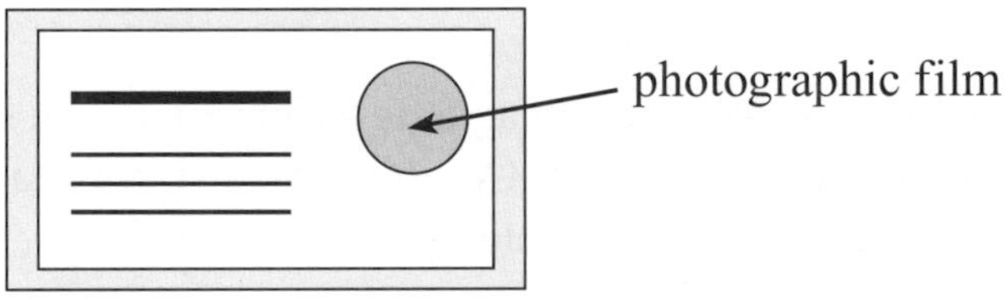

photographic film

a) i) Energy is transferred when the X-rays cause the chemical reaction in the badge. State the source and observer for this energy transfer.

....

[1]

ii) Describe the energy transfers involved in this process, from source to observer.

....

....

[2]

b) Give **one** other example of electromagnetic waves transferring energy from a source to an observer.

....

....

[1]

[Total 4 marks]

Uses of EM Waves

Tick the appropriate boxes to sort the radio wave facts from the fiction.

	True	False
Long-wave radio waves can be transmitted across long distances.	☐	☐
Long-wave radio waves bend and follow the curve of the Earth's surface.	☐	☐
Short-wave radio waves can only be used over short distances.	☐	☐
Wireless headsets use short-wave radio waves to transfer information.	☐	☐

1 Electromagnetic waves have a variety of different uses. (Grade 4-6)

a) Draw lines to match each type of electromagnetic radiation on the left to its use on the right.

| Ultraviolet | | photography |

| Visible light | | satellite communications |

| Infrared | | fluorescent lights |

| Radio waves | | security lights |

[2]

b) Give **two** examples of infrared waves being used to transfer information.

1. ....

2. ....

[2]

c) A camper has bought a device that filters and sterilises water so he can drink it.
The device uses electromagnetic radiation to sterilise the water.
What is the most likely type of radiation that the device would use?

☐ **A** gamma rays ☐ **B** ultraviolet ☐ **C** infrared ☐ **D** microwaves

[1]

[Total 5 marks]

Section 18 — Waves and the Electromagnetic Spectrum

2 A man uses a security pen to mark his belongings. The security pen contains fluorescent ink which cannot be seen in visible light.

Grade 4-6

a) Which of the following is true for fluorescent ink?

☐ **A** Fluorescent ink emits radio waves after it absorbs ultraviolet light.

☐ **B** Fluorescent ink emits ultraviolet light after it absorbs visible light.

☐ **C** Fluorescent ink emits visible light after it absorbs ultraviolet light.

☐ **D** Fluorescent ink emits ultraviolet light after it absorbs radio waves.

[1]

b) Explain how the security ink can be used to find the man's property if it is stolen.

....

....

....

[2]

c) Give **one** other example of where fluorescence is used in security.

....

[1]

[Total 4 marks]

3 **Figure 1** shows an X-ray image of a skull.

Grade 6-7

Figure 1

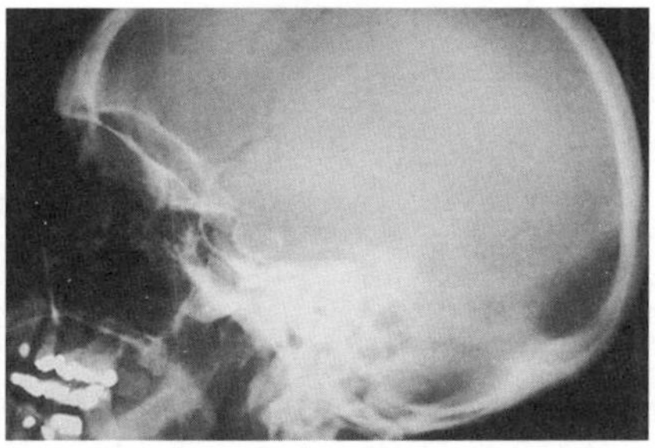

a) Explain how X-rays are used to form images like **Figure 1**.

....

....

....

....

[3]

b) Give **one** other non-medical use of X-rays.

....

[1]

[Total 4 marks]

Section 18 — Waves and the Electromagnetic Spectrum

4 A police helicopter has an infrared camera attached to its base. *Grade 6-7*

   a) Describe how an infrared camera works.

....

....

....

                                                   [2]

   b) Explain the advantages of using an infrared camera rather than a normal camera when searching for criminals at night.

....

....

....

....

                                                   [3]

[Total 5 marks]

5 A student uses a microwave oven to cook a jacket potato on a glass plate. *Grade 6-7*

   a) Describe how microwaves cook the potato in the microwave oven.

....

....

....

                                                   [3]

   b) Explain why the glass plate does not get as hot as the potato when the microwave oven is used.

....

....

....

                                                   [2]

   c) Microwaves can also be used to communicate with satellites. Explain why the microwaves used for communications must have different wavelengths to those used in microwave ovens.

....

....

....

....

                                                   [4]

[Total 9 marks]

Section 18 — Waves and the Electromagnetic Spectrum

6 Walkie-talkies use radio waves to communicate between each other. When a person speaks into the microphone, it creates an electric current. When the walkie-talkie receives a message, the microphone becomes a loudspeaker and converts electrical current into sound waves.

a) Briefly describe the steps involved for the creation, transmission and reception of a radio wave between a pair of walkie-talkies. You do not need to describe how microphones or loudspeakers work.

....

....

....

....

....

....

....

....

[6]

b)* A family from northern England are on holiday in France. Explain why they are unable to listen to their local FM radio station from back home, but are still able to listen to the same long-wave radio broadcasts as they do at home.

....

....

....

....

....

....

....

....

....

....

[6]

[Total 12 marks]

Exam Practice Tip

In the exams, you may be asked to explain why a given electromagnetic wave is suited to a particular use. So make sure you understand the properties of the different electromagnetic wave types, and know some of their most common uses.

The Model of the Atom

Warm-Up

Which of the following best describes the typical size of an atom?

☐ 1 mm   ☐ 1×10^{-5} m   ☐ 1×10^{-10} m   ☐ 1×10^{-20} m

1   Rutherford came up with a new model of the atom as a result of his scattering experiment.   [Grade 4-6]

a)   Name and describe the model that this model replaced.

....

....

[2]

b)   State **one** property of Rutherford's model of the atom. Describe the observation from
     Rutherford's scattering experiment that provided evidence for this property.

Property: ....

Observation: ....

....

[2]

[Total 4 marks]

2   **Figure 1** is an incomplete table showing the relative
     charges of the subatomic particles in an atom.   [Grade 4-6]

Figure 1

Particle	Proton	Neutron	Electron
Relative charge	....	....	−1

a)   Complete **Figure 1**.

[2]

b)   Describe how these subatomic particles are arranged in the atom.

....

....

[2]

c)   An iron atom has 26 protons. State the number of electrons in an iron atom
     and use this to explain the overall charge of the atom.

....

....

....

[2]

[Total 6 marks]

Electron Energy Levels

Warm-Up

Choose from the labels on the left to fill in the blanks on the right.
You do not need to use all of the words.

other electrons   varying

the nucleus

fixed

loops   shells

In Bohr's atomic model, electrons orbit

.... at .... distances

called energy levels or ....

1   Niels Bohr suggested that electrons can move between energy levels.   **Grade 4-6**

a) Describe how an inner electron can move between energy levels.

....

....

....

[2]

b) State the name of the type of particle created when an atom loses or gains outer electrons.

....

[1]

c) State the relative charge on the particle if it is created by an atom losing an outer electron.

....

[1]

[Total 4 marks]

2   A scientist is investigating the radiation emitted from a hydrogen discharge lamp. Inside
the lamp, electrons in hydrogen atoms are constantly being excited to higher energy levels
and then falling to lower levels. He finds that excited electrons falling back to the first
energy level release ultraviolet radiation (frequency $\sim 3 \times 10^{15}$ Hz). Excited electrons
falling back to the second energy level release visible light (frequency $\sim 5 \times 10^{14}$ Hz).   **Grade 7-9**

Explain why electrons falling to the first energy level of hydrogen release electromagnetic
radiation with a higher frequency than those falling to the second energy level.

....

....

....

....

....

....

[Total 4 marks]

Isotopes and Nuclear Radiation

The standard notation used to represent atoms is shown. Use the words below to correctly fill in the labels. You don't have to use every phrase, but each phrase can only be used — once.

$$^A_Z X$$

electron number

neutron number

mass number

element symbol

charge   atomic number

1   **Figure 1** shows a smoke detector. Smoke detectors contain radioactive isotopes. These isotopes are unstable and undergo radioactive decay to become more stable. They do this by emitting nuclear radiation.

Figure 1

a)   State what is meant by isotopes of an element.

....

....

[2]

b)   Some nuclear radiation is ionising.
State **three** types of ionising radiation emitted by radioactive decay.

....

....

[3]

c)   The unstable isotope in the smoke detector releases a particle made up of two protons and two neutrons from its nucleus.

i)   State the name of this type of decay.

....

[1]

ii) State and explain the range in air of the released particle.

....

....

[2]

[Total 8 marks]

Section 19 — Radioactivity

2   A student carries out an experiment to investigate two different radioactive sources. Her experiment is shown in **Figure 2**. She changes the material between the source and the Geiger-Muller tube and measures the count rate. **Figure 3** shows her results.

Figure 2

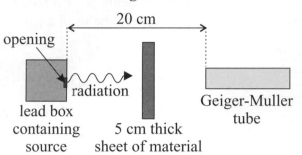

Figure 3

| Material | Count rate (counts per minute) | |
	Source A	Source B
No material	854	1203
Paper	847	1200
Aluminium	6	1199
Lead	5	280

a) Deduce the type of radiation source A emits.

....

[1]

b) State what kind of radiation source B emits. Explain your answer.

....

....

....

[3]

[Total 4 marks]

3   One isotope of sodium is $^{23}_{11}$Na.

a) Write down the nucleon number of this isotope.

....

[1]

b) Calculate the number of neutrons in the sodium nucleus.

Number of neutrons = ...

[1]

c) Which of the following is another isotope of sodium?

☐ **A** $^{11}_{23}$Na   ☐ **B** $^{11}_{24}$Na   ☐ **C** $^{23}_{12}$Na   ☐ **D** $^{24}_{11}$Na

[1]

d) An isotope of neon is $^{23}_{10}$Ne. State whether or not the charge on the neon isotope's nucleus is different to the charge on the nucleus of the sodium isotope. Explain your answer.

....

....

....

[2]

[Total 5 marks]

3   The activity of a radioisotope is 8800 Bq. Six hours later, the activity has fallen to 1100 Bq.   *Grade 6-7*

a) Calculate how many half-lives have passed during the six hours.

Number of half-lives = ...
[3]

b) Calculate the radioisotope's half-life.

Half-life = ... hour(s)
[1]

[Total 4 marks]

4   A radioactive sample has a **50** second half-life. The initial activity of the sample is 120 Bq.   *Grade 7-9*

a) Complete the graph in **Figure 3** to show how the activity will change in the first 150 seconds.

Figure 3

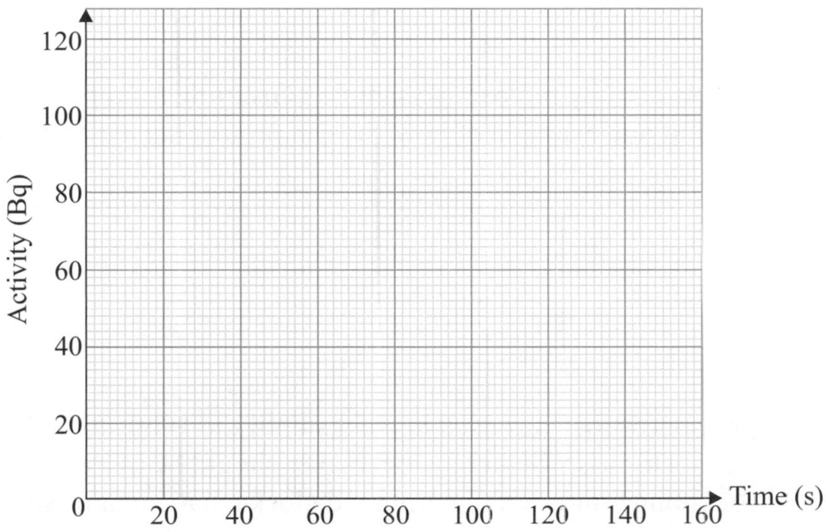

b) Predict, using your graph in **Figure 3**, the activity of the sample after 40 seconds.

Activity = ... Bq
[1]

c) Estimate the activity after 200 s. Give your answer to one significant figure.
Explain why this estimate is less likely to be correct than your prediction in part b).

....

....

....
[4]

[Total 7 marks]

Exam Practice Tip

Half-life and activity are really important things to get your head around — they're a key thing to mention when talking about any radioactive substance. Remember that every activity-time graph showing radioactive decay has the same shape — radioactive decay is a random process, but by looking at lots of nuclei you can make fairly accurate estimates.

Background Radiation and Contamination

1 Name **two** sources of background radiation.

Grade 4-6

1. ....

2. ....

[Total 2 marks]

2 A scientist is reviewing the safety procedures to be used in her lab. She is concerned about **contamination** and **irradiation**.

Grade 6-7

a) Explain the difference between contamination and irradiation.

....

....

....

....

[2]

b) The scientist is using a low activity radioactive sample. Give **one** example of how she can protect herself from irradiation and **one** example of how she can protect herself from contamination.

Irradiation: ....

Contamination: ....

[2]

[Total 4 marks]

3* Radium-226 is an alpha source that was used in clocks until the 1960s to make the hands and numbers glow. Discuss whether a clockmaker should be more concerned about irradiation or contamination when repairing old clocks that contain radium.

Grade 7-9

....

....

....

....

....

....

....

....

....

....

....

[Total 6 marks]

Section 19 — Radioactivity

Energy Transfers and Systems

1 Which of the following is correct for a closed system?

- [ ] **A** Energy into the system is always larger than energy out of the system.
- [ ] **B** Energy out of the system is always larger than energy into the system.
- [ ] **C** The net change of energy in a closed system is always zero.
- [ ] **D** Closed systems can only be changed by heating.

[Total 1 mark]

2 A filament bulb is connected to a battery, shown in **Figure 1**. You can assume that the wires connecting them have zero resistance. Complete the diagram in **Figure 2** to show the energy transfers that occur when the bulb in connected to the battery.

Figure 1

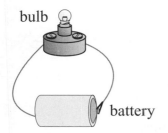

bulb

battery

Figure 2

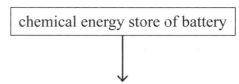

chemical energy store of battery

[Total 3 marks]

3 An 80.0 g apple is a one-object system. The apple is hanging from a branch.

a) i) The apple falls from the branch. It reaches a speed of 7.00 m/s just before it hits the ground. Calculate the energy in the apple's kinetic energy store just before it hits the ground.

Energy = ... J

[3]

ii) State what causes the energy transfer within this system.

[1]

b) Assuming that there was no air resistance, calculate the height the apple fell from. (Gravitational field strength = 10 N/kg.)

Height = ... m

[4]

[Total 7 marks]

Work Done and Power

Warm-Up

Complete the sentences below using the words or phrases from the box.
You can only use each option once and you do not need to use every option.

As a rubber ball falls, it experiences a .... due to ....

.... is done on the ball and .... is transferred from the ball's

.... energy store to its .... energy store.

| force | work | chemical potential | | kinetic | gravity |
| elastic potential | energy | | gravitational potential | heating | |

1 Which of these is the definition of power? (Grade 4-6)

☐ **A** Power is the total work done by an object.

☐ **B** Power is the rate of energy transfer.

☐ **C** Power is the total energy transferred to an object.

☐ **D** Power is the minimum work done to an object to cause it to move.

[Total 1 mark]

2 A student is investigating the work done by different washing machines during a standard washing cycle. **Figure 1** shows the manufacturer's data about three machines. (Grade 6-7)

Figure 1

Machine	Power	Time needed
A	600 W	125 minutes
B	400 W	160 minutes
C	....	125 minutes

a) Calculate the work done by machine A during its standard washing cycle.
Give your answer in kJ.

Work done = ... kJ
[4]

b) Machine C's standard cycle lasts for 125 minutes. It does 3 930 000 J of work in that time.
Complete the table in **Figure 1** by calculating the power of machine C.

[2]
[Total 6 marks]

3 A woman pushes a 20 kg wheelbarrow 15 m along a flat path using a horizontal force of 50 N.

Grade 6-7

a) i) State the equation that links work done, force applied and distance moved in the direction of the force.

....

[1]

ii) Calculate the work done by the woman.

Work done = ... J

[2]

b) Work has to be done against the frictional forces acting on the wheel of the wheelbarrow. Explain the effect this has on the temperature of the wheel.

....

....

....

[2]

[Total 5 marks]

4 A mechanic replaces a worn out engine of a car with a new, more efficient one. The old engine had a useful output power of 52 kW and an efficiency of 25%. The new engine has an efficiency of 30%.

Grade 7-9

a) Calculate the useful output power of the new engine. You can assume that the input power of both engines is the same.

Output power = ... W

[5]

b) Explain the effect replacing the engine will have on the time taken for the car to accelerate from rest to 20 m/s.

....

....

....

....

....

[3]

[Total 8 marks]

Section 20 — Forces and Energy

Forces

1   Forces are caused by interactions between objects.   (Grade 4-6)

a) Forces can be split into contact and non-contact forces.

   i) Describe what is meant by a 'contact force'.

....

....

[1]

   ii) Give **two** examples of a contact force.

    1. ....

    2. ....

[2]

b) Give **one** example of a non-contact force.

....

[1]

[Total 4 marks]

2   **Figure 1** shows four runners who are running in windy weather.   (Grade 4-6)
Which runner is experiencing the largest horizontal resultant force?

Figure 1

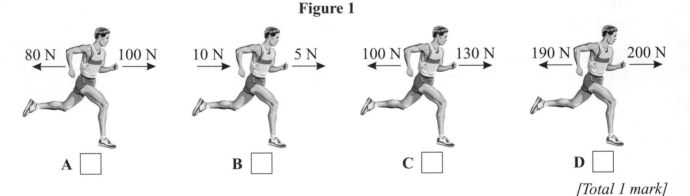

   80 N   100 N   10 N   5 N   100 N   130 N   190 N   200 N

    A ☐   **B** ☐   **C** ☐   **D** ☐

[Total 1 mark]

3   **Figure 2** shows a toy car. The weight of the car is 20 N. As it accelerates, it experiences   (Grade 6-7)
a driving force of 30 N. There is a 5 N resistive force acting against the motion of
the car. Add arrows to **Figure 2** to create a free body force diagram for the car.

Figure 2

[Total 2 marks]

Section 20 — Forces and Energy

4   **Figure 3** shows an incomplete diagram of the forces acting on a ladder leaning against a wall. There is no friction between the ladder and the wall but there is friction between the ladder and the ground.

Figure 3

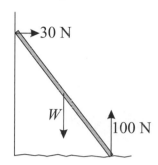

a) Complete **Figure 3** by drawing the missing frictional force.

[2]

b) Using **Figure 3**, determine the weight of the ladder, W.

Weight = ... N

[1]

[Total 3 marks]

5   **Figure 4** shows a pair of identical magnets. There is a force of repulsion between them.

Figure 4

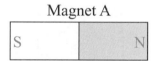   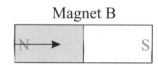

a) The arrow in **Figure 4** shows the force exerted on magnet B by magnet A. Complete the diagram in **Figure 4** by drawing another arrow representing the force that magnet B exerts on magnet A.

[2]

b) Explain what is causing the force between the two magnets.

....

....

[1]

c) Magnet B is replaced by a much stronger magnet.
The strength of magnet A and the orientation of the magnets remains the same.
Describe how you would redraw the arrows on the diagram to show this new force interaction.

....

....

[2]

[Total 5 marks]

Exam Practice Tip

Make sure you get your head around the difference between an interaction pair and a free body force diagram.
Free body force diagrams show the forces acting on a single object, whereas interaction pairs act on different objects.

Section 20 — Forces and Energy

Forces and Vector Diagrams

Find the sizes of the horizontal and vertical components of the force shown on the right. Each side of a square represents 1 N.

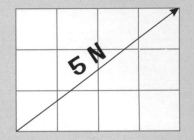

Horizontal component = ... N

Vertical component = ... N

1   **Figure 1** shows a girl on a swing. Her weight of 500 N acts vertically downwards and a tension force of 250 N acts on the ropes at an angle of 30° to the horizontal.

Figure 1   **Figure 2**

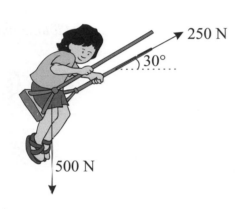

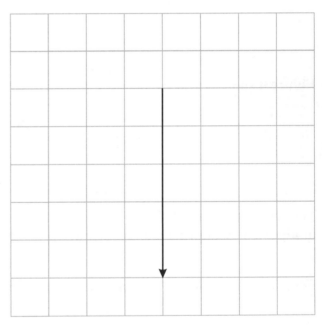

a) **Figure 2** shows an incomplete scale drawing for the forces acting on the girl. Only the girl's weight has been drawn so far. Calculate the scale used in the drawing.

.... cm = ... N
[1]

b) Complete the scale drawing in **Figure 2** to find the magnitude of the resultant force acting on the girl.

Magnitude = ... N
[2]

[Total 3 marks]

2 One of the events at a school sports day is a three-way tug of war.
Three teams each pull on a rope, all three of which are attached to a metal
ring. **Figure 3** shows the forces exerted on the ring. It is not drawn to scale.

Figure 3

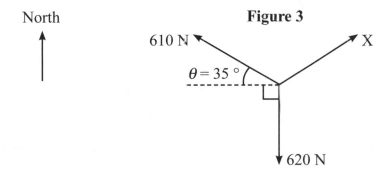

North

610 N   X

$\theta = 35°$

620 N

The ring is in equilibrium and does not move. Use the grid in **Figure 4** to create a
scale drawing to determine the magnitude and direction as a bearing of force X.

Figure 4

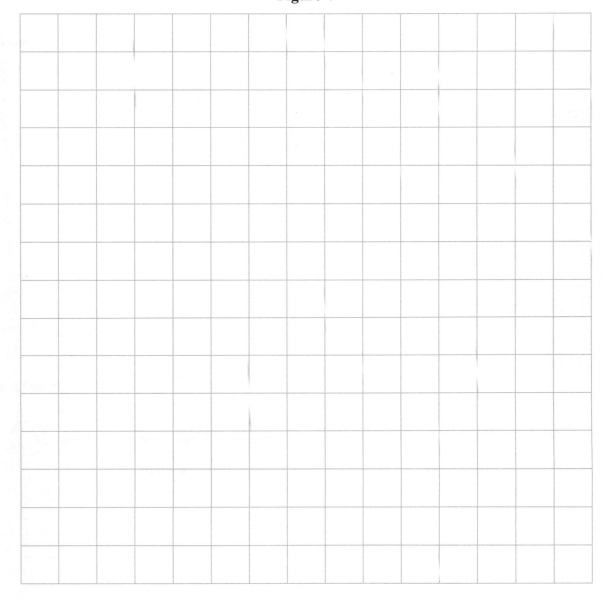

Magnitude of force X = ... N

Direction = ... °

[Total 5 marks]

Section 20 — Forces and Energy

Current and Circuits

Warm-Up

Fill in the blanks in these sentences with the words below.
You don't have to use every word, but each word can only be used once.

.... is the rate of flow of electric charge (electrons) around a circuit.

The driving force that pushes current around a circuit is called the ....

A current will flow around a circuit if the circuit is .... and there is a

source of ....

The current flowing through a component .... when the potential difference

across it increases or when the resistance of the component ....

| coulomb | energy | current | potential difference |
| potential difference | decreases | closed | increases |

---

1   **Figure 1** shows a circuit symbol.   (Grade 4-6)

Figure 1

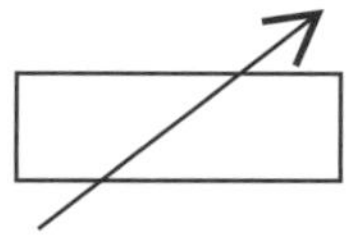

The circuit symbol shown is a

☐   **A** resistor.

☐   **B** variable resistor.

☐   **C** thermistor.

☐   **D** fuse.

[Total 1 mark]

---

2   A current of 3.5 A flows through a simple circuit containing a battery and a resistor.   (Grade 6-7)

a) Calculate how much charge passes through the light bulb in 120 seconds.

Charge = ... C

[3]

b) Calculate how long it will take for 770 C to pass through the light bulb.

Time = ... s

[3]

[Total 6 marks]

Potential Difference and Resistance

1 A kettle needs 276 000 J of energy to be electrically transferred to it in order to bring water to the boil. It is connected to the mains supply which has a voltage of 230 V. **Grade 6-7**

a) Calculate the amount of charge that passes through the kettle to bring the water to the boil.

Charge = ... C

[3]

b) A toaster is connected to the same mains supply. When a slice of bread is toasted, the charge that passes through the toaster is 1000 C.

Calculate the energy transferred to toast the slice of bread. Give your answer in kJ.

Energy transferred = ... kJ

[2]

[Total 5 marks]

2 When a potential difference of 18 V is applied across a resistor, a current of 3 A flows through it. **Grade 6-7**

a) Calculate the resistance of the resistor. State the units of your answer.

Resistance = ... Units ....

[4]

b) Over time, the current through the resistor begins to decrease. Explain why this happens.

....

....

....

....

....

[4]

[Total 8 marks]

Investigating Components

1　Voltmeters and ammeters are used to investigate circuits.　(Grade 4-6)

a)　A voltmeter should always be connected

☐　**A**　in series with the component.

☐　**B**　in series with the source of potential difference.

☐　**C**　in parallel with a resistor.

☒　**D**　in parallel with the component.

[1]

b)　**Figure 1** shows a circuit. Draw an ammeter in an appropriate place on the diagram to measure the current flowing through the bulb.

Figure 1

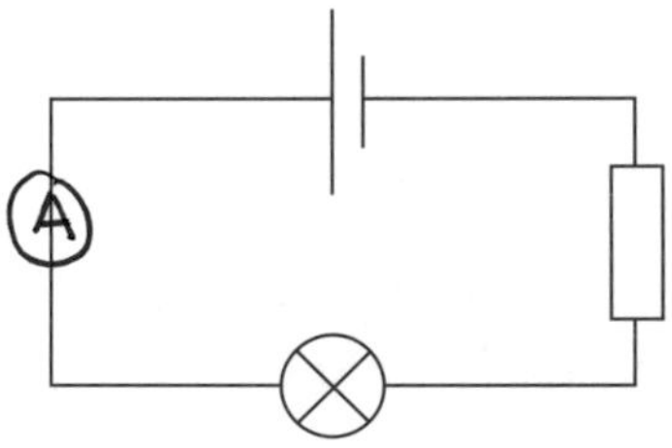

[1]

[Total 2 marks]

PRACTICAL

2*　A student is investigating the resistance of a diode. He sets up the circuit shown in **Figure 2**.　(Grade 7-9)

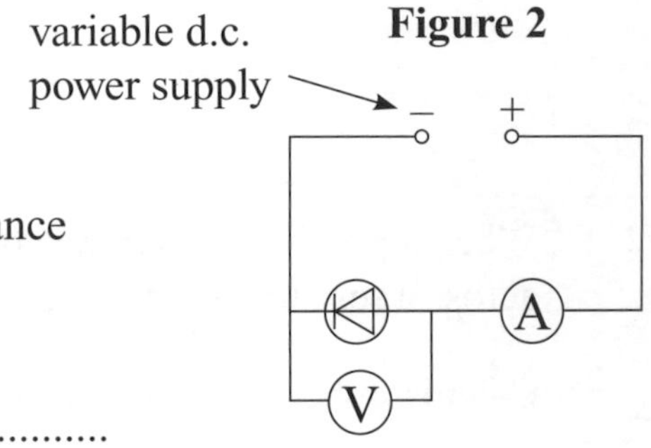

Describe how he could use this circuit to investigate the resistance of the diode. Include a discussion of the steps he should take to make sure his results are accurate and repeatable.

variable d.c. power supply　**Figure 2**

....

....

....

....

....

....

....

....

....

....

[Total 6 marks]

Circuit Devices

Draw lines to match each circuit symbol to the name of the component that it's representing.

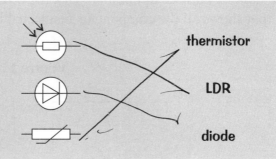

thermistor

LDR

diode

1 The resistance of a thermistor changes depending on its surroundings. Grade 4-6

a) State what happens to the resistance of a thermistor as the surrounding temperature increases.

....

[1]

b) Give **one** example of a device that uses a thermistor.

....

[1]

[Total 2 marks]

2 Filament bulbs are a common circuit component. Grade 6-7

a) Which is the correct *I-V* graph for a filament bulb?

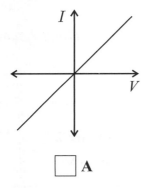 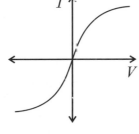 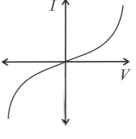 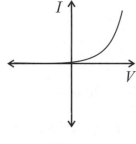

☐ **A**   ☐ **B**   ☐ **C**   ☒ **D**

[1]

b) Explain why the *I-V* graph for a filament bulb has this shape.

....

....

....

[2]

[Total 3 marks]

Exam Practice Tip

You'll need to know the *I-V* graphs for resistors, wires and diodes too, and whether they're linear or non-linear graphs. Plus, you'll need to be able to explain how the gradient of an *I-V* graph relates to the resistance of the component.

 ☐   ☐   ☐

Section 21 — Electricity and Circuits

Series and Parallel Circuits

1 **Figure 1** shows a number of circuits. Tick the box below the diagram that shows all the components connected in series.

Grade 4-6

Figure 1

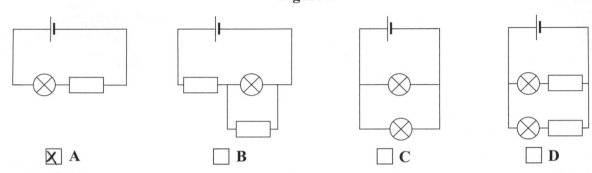

☒ A ☐ B ☐ C ☐ D

[Total 1 mark]

2 Draw a circuit diagram consisting of a cell and two LDRs connected in parallel.

Grade 4-6

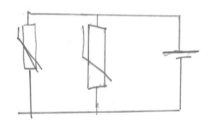

[Total 2 marks]

3 In the circuit in **Figure 2**, the reading on the ammeter is 75 mA.

Grade 6-7

a) Calculate the total resistance of the two resistors.

Figure 2

3 V

10 Ω   30 Ω

Resistance = ...2 0.......... Ω
[1]

b) Calculate the potential difference across the 30 Ω resistor.

Potential Difference = ...1.......... V
[3]

[Total 4 marks]

4* Explain why adding resistors in series with each other increases the total resistance of the resistors, whilst adding resistors in parallel with each other decreases the total resistance of the resistors.

Grade 7-9

....

....

....

....

....

....

....

....

....

....

....

....

[Total 6 marks]

PRACTICAL

5 A student is investigating series and parallel circuits, using bulbs which are labelled as having the same resistance. She sets up the circuit shown in **Figure 3**.

Grade 7-9

Figure 3

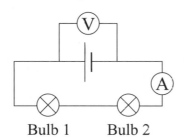

Bulb 1   Bulb 2

The voltmeter reads 12 V and the ammeter reads 0.25 A.
The student uses these values to calculate the resistance of each bulb.

a) Calculate the resistance of each bulb, assuming that the bulbs do have the same resistance.

Resistance = ... Ω

[3]

Section 21 — Electricity and Circuits

b) The student then adds a third bulb to the circuit, as shown in **Figure 4**.

Figure 4

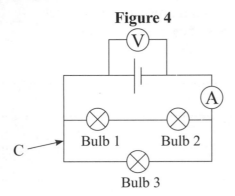

i) Assuming that bulb 3 is identical to bulbs 1 and 2, find the new current through the ammeter.

Current = ... A

[2]

ii) The student observes that bulb 3 is brighter than bulbs 1 and 2. Explain why.

....

....

[2]

c) The student then adds a resistor to the circuit in **Figure 4**, at the point marked C.

i) Describe the effect of this on the current through the ammeter.

....

[1]

ii) State how this affects the brightness of the three bulbs.

....

....

[2]

d) When the student's teacher marks her experiment, he says she should have measured the potential difference across and the current through each bulb throughout the experiment. Give **two** reasons why.

....

....

....

[2]

[Total 12 marks]

Exam Practice Tip

Although we talk about series and parallel circuits as separate things, real circuits are often a mix — you might get a question where some components are connected in series with each other, but where there's more than one branch to the circuit. Don't panic, just remember that the rules of parallel circuits apply when you're looking at the different branches, and the rules of series circuits apply when you're looking at the components connected along one branch.

Energy in Circuits

1 Which of the following describes the energy transferred to an electric heater connected to the mains?

Grade 4-6

- [ ] **A** Energy is transferred electrically to the kinetic energy store of the heater.
- [ ] **B** Energy is transferred by heating to the electrostatic energy store of the heater.
- [ ] **C** Energy is transferred by heating to the gravitational potential energy store of the heater.
- [ ] **D** Energy is transferred electrically to the thermal energy store of the heater.

[Total 1 mark]

2 A hairdryer contains of a motor which turns a fan and a heating element.

Grade 6-7

a) State **one** part of the hairdryer where the heating effect of a current is **useful**.

....

[1]

b) State **one** part of the hairdryer where the heating effect of a current is **not useful**.

....

[1]

c) The hairdryer becomes less efficient the longer it is left on for. Explain why.

....

....

....

[3]

[Total 5 marks]

3 A kettle is filled with a litre of water from the cold tap.

Grade 6-7

a) It takes 355 000 J of energy to bring a litre of water to the boil. The kettle is attached to the mains, at 230 V, and the current through the kettle is 12 A. Calculate how long it should take the kettle to boil, to the nearest second.

Time = ... s

[3]

b) State **one** assumption that you made in order to answer part a).

....

....

[1]

[Total 4 marks]

Power in Circuits

1 A child is playing with a toy car. The car is powered by a battery and has two speed settings — fast and slow.

a) The child sets the speed to slow and drives the car for 20 seconds. The power of the car at this speed is 50 W. Calculate the energy transferred by the car.

Energy transferred = ... J

[3]

b) The child now sets the speed to fast. The power of the car at this speed is 75 W. Explain why the battery runs down more quickly when the car is set at a higher speed.

....

....

[2]

[Total 5 marks]

2 Fans use a motor to turn a set of blades.

a) A 75 W ceiling fan in an office is powered by the mains supply at 230 V. Calculate the current supplied to the fan.

Current = ... A

[3]

b) A smaller fan on someone's desk runs from a computer's USB port. It has a power of 2.5 W, and draws a current of 0.50 A. Calculate its resistance.

Resistance = ... Ω

[3]

The ceiling fan from part a) breaks and the company investigate replacing it with a standing fan. They look at three models, A-C, summarised in **Figure 1**.

Figure 1

Model	Power rating / W	Customer reviews
A	50	very noisy
B	40	breaks frequently, a bit small
C	45	quiet and reliable

c) i) Give the model that transfers energy at the fastest rate. ....

[1]

ii) Explain why your answer to part c) i) may not be the most efficient fan for cooling the office.

....

....

[2]

[Total 9 marks]

Electricity in the Home

Warm-Up

In the table below, put a tick next to each statement to show whether it applies to direct current or alternating current.

	Direct current	Alternating current
Describes the current supplied by a battery		
Produced by a voltage that constantly changes direction		
Describes the current supplied by the UK mains		
Produced by a voltage with a constant direction		

1 Most houses in the UK are connected to the mains supply. *(Grade 4-6)*

a) State the potential difference and frequency of the UK mains electricity supply.

....

[1]

b) A kettle is plugged into the mains with a three-core cable containing a live wire, a neutral wire and an earth wire.

i) State the colours of the live, neutral, and earth wires.

Live: ....

Neutral: ....

Earth: ....

[2]

ii) Complete the table in **Figure 1** to show the sizes of the potential differences between the wires that make up the three-core cable.

Figure 1

Wires	Potential difference / V
Live wire and neutral wire	....
Neutral wire and earth wire	....
Earth wire and live wire	....

[3]

[Total 6 marks]

2 A radio develops a fault such that the live wire is in electrical contact with the neutral wire.

Grade 6-7

Explain whether you think the radio will work while this fault remains.

....

....

....

....

[Total 3 marks]

3 The cable that connects an iron to the mains supply has become worn with use. There is no insulation covering part of the live wire. The iron is plugged in, but switched off.

Grade 6-7

a) State **two** purposes of the insulation that covers the live wire.

....

....

....

[2]

b) A man switches on the iron and touches the exposed live wire. He receives an electric shock. Explain why he receives an electric shock. You should refer to the electrical potential of the man in your answer.

....

....

....

....

[3]

c) The the socket is switched off and the iron is unplugged.
Explain whether there is still a danger of the man receiving an electric shock from the plug socket.

....

....

....

....

[3]

[Total 8 marks]

> **Exam Practice Tip**
> The voltage-time graph for an alternating current has a similar shape to the wave shown on p.185. The frequency of an alternating current is how many cycles it completes per second, where one cycle is, for example, from one crest to the next crest (or from one trough to the next trough). It's measured in Hz, just like wave frequency.

Fuses and Earthing

1 **Figure 1** shows an old-fashioned household fuse box.

Figure 1

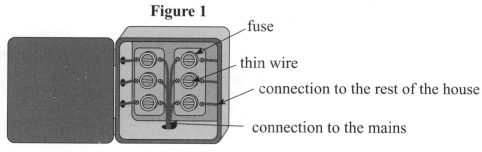

- fuse
- thin wire
- connection to the rest of the house
- connection to the mains

a) Explain why houses have fuse boxes.

....

[1]

b) In old-fashioned fuse boxes like this, home-owners sometimes replaced old fuses with pennies. Explain why replacing fuses with pennies like this was dangerous.

....

....

[1]

c) Most modern houses uses circuit breakers, rather than fuse boxes.
Give **one** advantage and **one** disadvantage of using circuit breakers instead of fuses.

Advantage: ....

Disadvantage: ....

[2]

[Total 4 marks]

2 Many electrical devices include an Earth wire. (Grade 6-7)

a) Explain how the earth wire and fuse work when a fault develops with a metal appliance.

....

....

....

....

[3]

b) The fuse in an electric heater is rated at 13 A. The fuse in a clock radio is rated at 3 A.
Suggest why these devices need fuses with different ratings.

....

....

....

[2]

[Total 6 marks]

Section 21 — Electricity and Circuits

Magnets and Magnetic Fields

1   All magnets produce magnetic fields.   (Grade 4-6)

   a)   Which of the following statements is correct for magnets?

      ☐   **A**   Like poles attract each other.

      ☐   **B**   Magnetic fields are weakest at the poles of a magnet.

      ☐   **C**   Unlike poles attract each other.

      ☐   **D**   Magnetic field lines go from the south pole to the north pole.

             [1]

   b)   **Figure 1** shows a bar magnet. Draw the magnetic field lines onto the diagram in **Figure 1**.

Figure 1

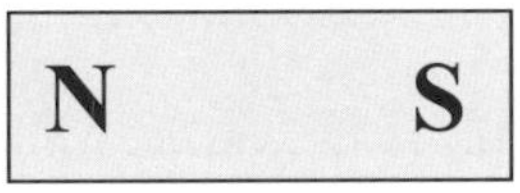

N   S

             [3]

   Two bar magnets are placed near to each other, as shown in **Figure 2**.

Figure 2

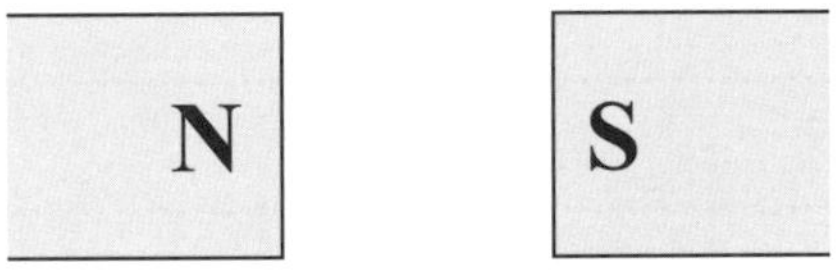

N   S

   c)   i)   A uniform magnetic field is created between them. Explain what is meant by a uniform field.

      ....

      ....

             [1]

      ii) Draw the uniform field between the two poles shown in **Figure 2**.

             [2]

             [Total 7 marks]

2 A student places two magnetic objects near to each other on a flat, frictionless surface. **Figure 3** shows their magnetic fields. The student then releases the objects at the same time.

Grade 6-7

Figure 3

State and explain the behaviour of the two objects once they are released.

....

....

....

[Total 3 marks]

3 A student wants to investigate the magnetic field of a horseshoe magnet, shown in **Figure 4**.

Grade 6-7

Figure 4

a) Describe how a compass could be used to determine the magnetic field pattern of the magnet.

....

....

....

....

....

....

....

....

....

....

....

....

[4]

b) State and explain what would happen to the compass if you were to move it far away from any magnets.

....

....

....

[2]

[Total 6 marks]

Exam Practice Tip

Iron filings can also be used to see the shape of a magnetic field — but remember, they won't show you its direction.

Section 22 — Magnetic Fields

Permanent and Induced Magnets

1 Magnets can be permanent or induced. *(Grade 4-6)*

a) Describe the difference between a permanent magnet and an induced magnet.

....

....

....

[2]

b) Name **two** magnetic materials.

1. ....

2. ....

[2]

c) State **one** everyday use of magnets.

....

[1]

[Total 5 marks]

2 A block of cobalt is held in place near to a bar magnet, as shown in **Figure 1**. *(Grade 6-7)*

Figure 1

N S		● P
bar magnet		cobalt

a) A steel paperclip is placed against the block of cobalt at point P, shown on **Figure 1**.
The paperclip sticks to the block of cobalt. Explain why this happens.

....

....

....

....

....

....

[3]

b) The bar magnet is removed. Explain what happens to the paperclip.

....

....

....

[2]

[Total 5 marks]

Electromagnetism and the Motor Effect

Warm-Up

The diagram shows a left hand being used for Fleming's left hand rule.
Using **three** of the labels below, label the thumb and fingers in the diagram.

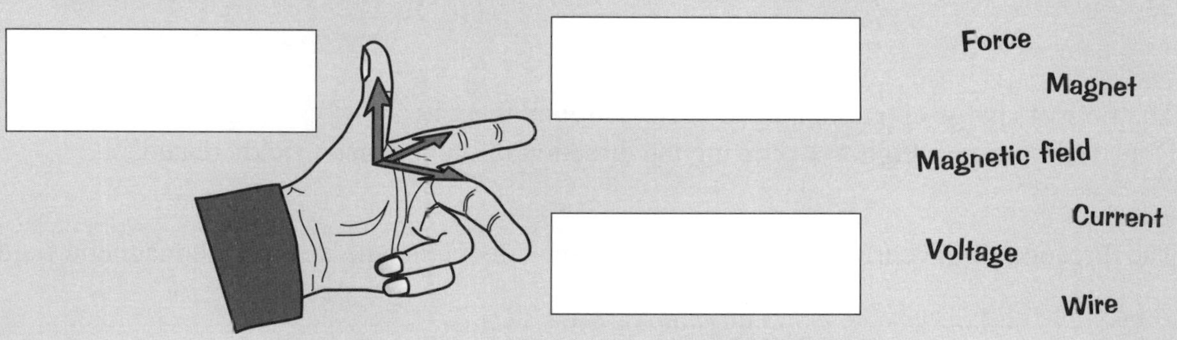

Force

Magnet

Magnetic field

Current

Voltage

Wire

1 A wire is placed between two magnets, as shown in **Figure 1**.
A current is flowing through the wire, in the direction shown.

Grade
4-6

Figure 1

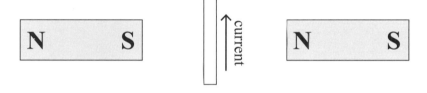

a) What will happen to the wire?

☐ **A** It will move to the left.

☐ **B** It will move away from you, into the paper.

☐ **C** It will move towards you, out of the paper.

☐ **D** It will remain stationary.

[1]

b) This effect is called the motor effect. Explain the cause of the motor effect.

....

....

[2]

c) State **three** factors which determine the magnitude of the force acting on the wire.

1. ....

2. ....

3. ....

[3]

[Total 6 marks]

2 **Figure 2** shows a wire which has a current flowing through it.
The arrow shows the direction of the current.

Figure 2

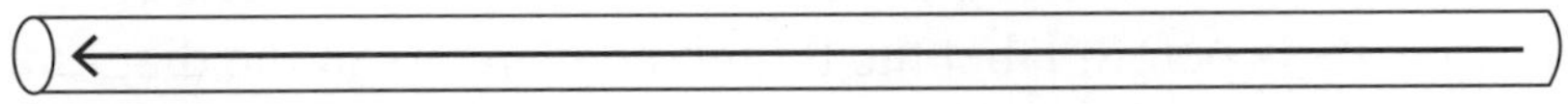

a) The flow of charge creates a magnetic field around the wire.
Draw field lines on **Figure 2** showing the direction of the magnetic field created.

[2]

b) The direction of the current is reversed. State the effect this will have on the magnetic field.

....

....

[1]

c) Give **one** way to increase the strength of the magnetic field produced by the wire.

....

[1]

[Total 4 marks]

3 A 0.75 m section of wire, carrying a current of 0.4 A, is placed into a magnetic field, shown
in **Figure 3**. When the wire is perpendicular to the field, it experiences a force of 1.2 N.

Figure 3

wire

S ● N

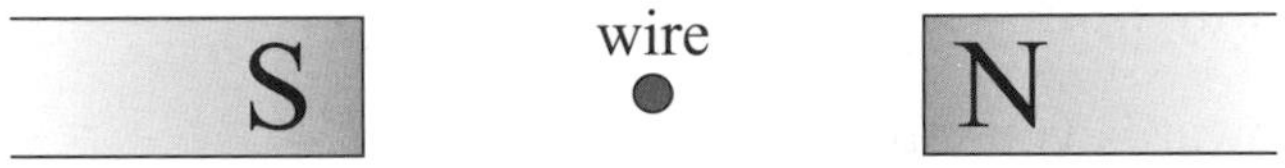

Calculate the magnetic flux density of the field. Give the correct unit in your answer.

Magnetic flux density = ...

Unit = ...

[Total 4 marks]

Exam Practice Tip

Don't get confused between which hand you're using for a situation. Use your right hand for finding the magnetic field
produced by a current-carrying conductor and your left hand for the force acting on a wire in a magnetic field.

Section 22 — Magnetic Fields

Solenoids and Electromagnetic Induction

For each statement, circle whether it is true (T) or false (F).

A single loop of current-carrying wire produces a magnetic field.	T / F
A solenoid is an example of a transformer.	T / F
An electromagnet can be turned on and off.	T / F
The magnetic field is weakest inside a solenoid.	T / F

1 This question is about statements 1 and 2, shown below. **Grade 4-6**

Statement 1: A potential difference is induced when an electrical conductor moves relative to a magnetic field.

Statement 2: A potential difference is induced when there is a change in the magnetic field around an electrical conductor.

Which of the following is correct?

☐ **A** Only statement 1 is true.

☐ **B** Only statement 2 is true.

☐ **C** Both statements 1 and 2 are true.

☐ **D** Neither statement 1 nor 2 is true.

[Total 1 mark]

2 Solenoids are an example of an electromagnet. **Grade 4-6**

a) State what is meant by an electromagnet.

....

....

[1]

b) i) Describe the magnetic field inside the centre of a solenoid.

....

....

[2]

ii) Describe the magnetic field of a solenoid outside of the solenoid.

....

....

[2]

[Total 5 marks]

3 A student sets up a simple circuit to measure the current generated when he moves a magnet in and out of a coil. The set-up of his apparatus is shown in **Figure 1**.

Figure 1

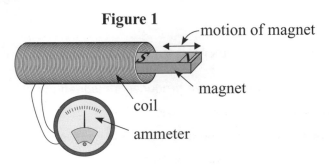

a) State and explain whether the set-up in **Figure 1** generates alternating or direct current.

....

....

....

....

[3]

b) State **three** ways to increase the potential difference induced by the set-up in **Figure 1**.

1. ....

2. ....

3. ....

[3]

[Total 6 marks]

4 A current-carrying solenoid has a magnetic field outside it similar to a bar magnet.

a) State how iron can be used to increase the magnetic field of the solenoid.

....

[1]

b) The north pole of a magnet is brought near to the current-carrying solenoid as shown in **Figure 2**. State whether the north pole is **attracted** or **repelled** by the solenoid. Explain your answer.

Figure 2

N

....

....

....

[3]

[Total 4 marks]

Transformers

For each option, circle the word that correctly completes each sentence.

Transformers consist of two coils of wire, wrapped around a(n) (plastic / iron) core.

Transformers can change the size of (alternating / direct) potential differences.

(Step-up / Step-down) transformers decrease the output potential difference.

(Step-up / Step-down) transformers decrease the output current.

1 A transformer is 100% efficient. The current through the primary coil is 20.0 A and the potential difference across it is 30.0 V. The potential difference across the secondary coil is 40.0 V. Calculate the current through the secondary coil.

Current = ... A

[Total 3 marks]

2* Transformers use electromagnetic induction to increase or decrease the potential difference that is supplied to them.

Explain how a step-up transformer uses electromagnetic induction to increase its output potential difference. Your answer should refer to the number of turns on each coil of the transformer.

....

....

....

....

....

....

....

....

....

....

....

[Total 6 marks]

Section 22 — Magnetic Fields

3   **Figure 1** shows a basic model of how the national grid uses step-up and step-down transformers to vary the potential difference and current of the electricity it transmits. The national grid often transmits electricity at 400 000 V.

Figure 1

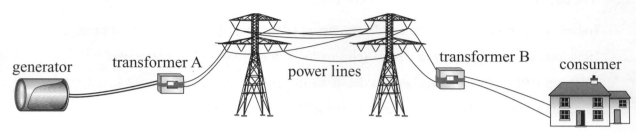

a) State what type of transformer the transformer's labelled A and B are.

Transformer A: ....

Transformer B: ....

[2]

b) The current generated in the secondary coil of any transformer creates its own magnetic field. Describe the direction of this magnetic field in relation to the magnetic field that caused it.

....

....

[1]

c)* Explain the advantages of using transformers and high-voltage cables to transfer large amounts of energy every second via the national grid. You should use equations to justify your answer.

....

....

....

....

....

....

....

....

....

....

[6]

[Total 9 marks]

Exam Practice Tip

The equation you need for question one will be given to you in the exam — you just have to choose the correct equation from the list. To work out which one to use, it might help to make a list of all the values you've been given.

Density

1 A 0.5 m^3 block of tungsten has a mass of 10 000 kg. Grade 4-6

a) i) Write down the equation that links density, mass and volume.

....

[1]

ii) Calculate the density of tungsten.

Density = ... kg/m^3

[2]

b) Calculate the mass of a 0.02 m^3 sample cut from the tungsten block.

Mass = ... kg

[2]

[Total 5 marks]

2 The titanium bar shown in **Figure 1** has a mass of 90.0 kg. Grade 6-7

Figure 1

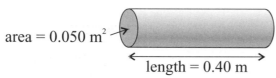

area = 0.050 m²
length = 0.40 m

Calculate the density of titanium.

Density = ... kg/m^3

[Total 3 marks]

PRACTICAL

3 A student uses the apparatus in **Figure 2** to calculate the volumes of different rings to determine what materials they are made from. Grade 6-7

Figure 2

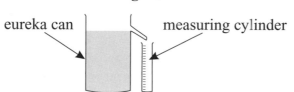

eureka can
measuring cylinder

The can is filled up to the spout so that when a ring is placed in the can, the displaced water flows into the measuring cylinder. **Figure 3** shows an incomplete table of the student's results.

Figure 3

Ring	Mass (g)	Water displaced (ml)	Material
A	5.7	0.30	....
B	2.7	0.60	....
C	3.0	0.30	....

One ring is made from gold, one is made from silver and the other is made from titanium.
Complete **Figure 3** using the following information:

Density of gold = 19 g/cm³   Density of silver = 10 g/cm³   Density of titanium = 4.5 g/cm³

[Total 5 marks]

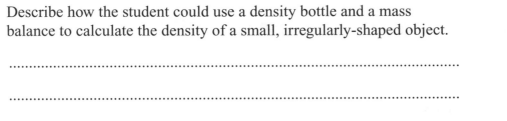

PRACTICAL

4   **Figure 4** shows a density bottle. When full, the density bottle holds a set volume of liquid that is accurately known.

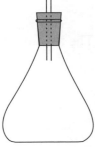

Figure 4

Describe how the student could use a density bottle and a mass balance to calculate the density of a small, irregularly-shaped object.

....

....

....

....

....

....

....

....

....

....

[Total 6 marks]

Exam Practice Tip

You may be asked about experiments you've never seen before in an exam, but don't panic. To get full marks, take your time to read all the information carefully and work out what's going on before attempting any questions.

Kinetic Theory and States of Matter

The images below show the particles in a substance when it is in three different states of matter. Label each image to show whether the substance is a solid, a liquid or a gas.

....

1 Draw a line to match the change of state on the left to its description on the right. (Grade 4-6)

| condensation | gas to liquid |

| sublimation | liquid to gas |

| evaporation | solid to gas |

[Total 1 mark]

2 The density of different states of matter varies. (Grade 4-6)

a) Which of the following statements is true about the different states of matter?

☐ **A** A liquid is usually less dense than a gas.

☐ **B** A liquid is usually more dense than a solid.

☐ **C** A solid is usually more dense than a gas.

☐ **D** A solid is usually less dense than a gas.

[1]

b) A student notices that ice cubes float when he puts them into a glass of water. This is because ice is less dense than liquid water. Explain what this suggests about the arrangement of the water molecules in each state.

....

....

....

....

[2]

[Total 3 marks]

3 A student leaves a sealed glass flask with 200 ml of purified water in it on a windowsill on a hot day. He checks the flask every hour and observes that the volume of liquid water decreases throughout the day.

Grade
4-6

a) Suggest why the volume of liquid water has decreased during the day.

....

[1]

b) Explain what happens to the total mass of the bottle and its contents during the day.

....

....

....

[2]

[Total 3 marks]

4 A student does an experiment to investigate methanol as it changes state. **Figure 1** shows their equipment. When the water bath is turned on, the water inside it begins to heat up.

Grade
6-7

Figure 1

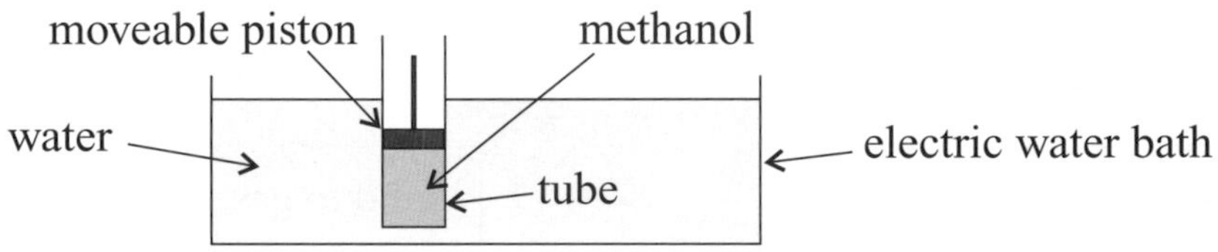

moveable piston   methanol

water ———→

tube

electric water bath

As the water is heated, the piston begins to move upwards. After a short time, the tube containing the methanol begins to fill with gas. Explain this behaviour in terms of the energy transfers and the particles that make up the methanol.

....

....

....

....

....

....

....

....

[Total 5 marks]

Exam Practice Tip

Remember that all changes of state are physical changes, not chemical changes. Chemical changes result in a new substance being created. During a change of state, the particles in a substance move and either get closer together or further apart. The particles themselves don't change, so a change of state has to be a physical change.

Specific Heat Capacity

Warm-Up

Which of the following is the correct definition of specific heat capacity? Tick **one** box.

The energy transferred when an object is burnt. ☐

The maximum amount of energy an object can store before it melts. ☐

The energy needed to raise 1 kg of a substance by 10 °C. ☐

The energy needed to raise 1 kg of a substance by 1 °C. ☐

PRACTICAL

1 A student uses the equipment listed below to investigate the specific heat capacity of different liquids.

- Insulated flask
- Power supply
- Thermometer
- Joulemeter
- Mass balance
- Immersion heater

a) Describe how the student could use the apparatus listed above to calculate the specific heat capacities of different liquids.

....

....

....

....

....

....

[5]

b) 15 kJ of energy was supplied to each sample. The student then recorded her results, shown in **Figure 1**. Complete **Figure 1** to show the specific heat capacity of liquid C.

Figure 1

Liquid	Mass (kg)	Temperature change (°C)	Specific heat capacity (J/kg °C)
A	0.30	12	4200
B	0.30	23	2200
C	0.30	25	....

[3]

[Total 8 marks]

Specific Latent Heat

1 **Figure 1** shows the mass and specific latent heat of vaporisation (SLH) of substances A-D. Which substance requires the most amount of energy to completely boil it?

Figure 1

		Mass (kg)	SLH (J/kg)
☐	A	1	1.5
☐	B	1	1.0
☐	C	2	1.5
☐	D	3	2.0

[Total 1 mark]

2 A student uses a freezer to freeze 0.50 kg of brine.

a) Define the term 'specific latent heat'.

....

....
[1]

b) Explain the difference between specific heat capacity and specific latent heat.

....

....
[1]

Figure 2 shows the temperature-time graph for brine as it was cooled.

Figure 2

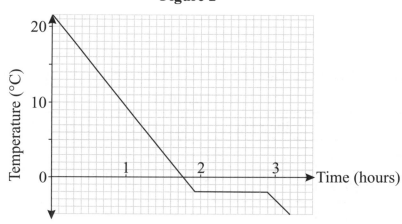

c) State the freezing point of brine.

Freezing point = ... °C
[1]

[Total 3 marks]

3 A student investigates the specific latent heat of water. They place 500 g of ice into an insulated beaker and use an immersion heater to heat the ice. They record the temperature of the water every 10 seconds. Their results are shown in **Figure 3**.

Figure 3

Time (s)	Temperature (°C)
0	0
10	0
20	0
30	0
40	0
50	0
60	7
70	21

Time (s)	Temperature (°C)
80	36
90	50
100	64
110	79
120	92
130	100
140	100
150	100

Figure 4

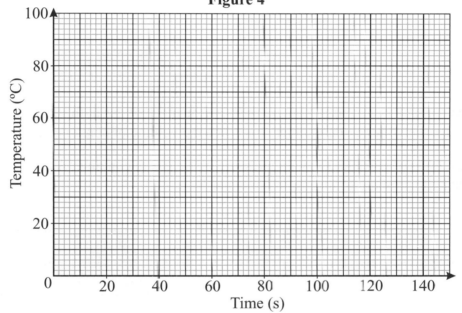

a) Draw the temperature-time graph for the student's results on **Figure 4**.

[2]

b) The immersion heater transfers 1.13 MJ of energy to the water once
   it has reached its boiling point to completely boil all of the water.
   Calculate the specific latent heat of vaporisation of water. Give your answer in MJ/kg.

Specific latent heat = ... MJ/kg

[3]

c) Explain, in terms of particles, the shape of the graph between 0 and 50 seconds.

....

....

....

[3]

[Total 8 marks]

Section 23 — Matter

Particle Motion in Gases

Circle the correct words or phrases below so that the sentences are correct.

The particles in a gas are always moving in <u>the same direction / random directions</u>.

A gas exerts a force on a container due to <u>collisions / radioactivity</u>.

The total force exerted by the particles per unit area is the gas <u>energy / pressure</u>.

1 Describe, in terms of particles, what is meant by the term absolute zero. **Grade 4-6**

....

....

....

[Total 1 mark]

2 Two sealed containers, A and B, contain the same quantity of gas at the same temperature. The volume of container A is twice the volume of container B. **Grade 6-7**

Explain, in terms of particles, why the pressure of the gas in container A is lower than the pressure of the gas in container B.

....

....

....

....

[Total 2 marks]

3 A gas is held in a sealed container with a fixed volume. The initial temperature of the gas is 295 K. **Grade 6-7**

a) Give the initial temperature of the gas in degrees Celsius.

.... °C
[1]

b) The container is heated over a Bunsen burner.
Describe and explain how this affects the pressure of the gas inside the container.

....

....

....

[3]
[Total 4 marks]

4 **Figure 1** shows four sealed containers. Each contains the same mass of a gas. In which container is the pressure of the gas the highest?

Figure 1

| Volume = 0.04 m³ | Volume = 0.04 m³ | Volume = 40 000 cm³ | Volume = 40 000 cm³ |
| Temperature = 10 °C | Temperature = 20 °C | Temperature = 283 K | Temperature = 30 °C |

☐ **A** ☐ **B** ☐ **C** ☐ **D**

[Total 1 mark]

5 A student investigates how varying the volume of a container full of a fixed mass of gas at a constant temperature affects the pressure of the gas. **Figure 2** is an incomplete table of his results.

Figure 2

Volume (m³)	Pressure (kPa)
8.0×10^{-4}	50
4.0×10^{-4}	100
2.5×10^{-4}	160
1.6×10^{-4}	....

Figure 3

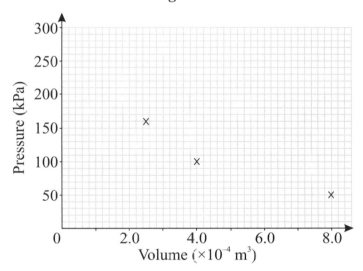

a) Complete **Figure 2** by calculating the missing pressure measurement.

[3]

b) Using information from **Figure 2**, complete the graph in **Figure 3** by plotting the missing data and drawing a line of best fit.

[2]

[Total 5 marks]

Exam Practice Tip

Remember, one degree on the Kelvin scale is the same size as one degree on the Celsius scale, but 0 K is much, much colder than 0 °C. A temperature in Kelvin will always have a higher value than the same temperature in Celsius.

Section 23 — Matter

Forces and Elasticity

1   A child is playing with a toy that contains a spring.   *(Grade 4-6)*

a) Give the minimum number of forces that need to be applied to the spring in order to stretch it.

....

[1]

b) When the spring is compressed, it distorts elastically.
Explain the difference between elastic and inelastic distortion.

....

....

....

[2]

c) i) State the equation that links the force exerted on a spring, its spring constant and its extension.

....

[1]

ii) A 20 N force stretches the spring by 8 cm. Calculate the spring constant of the spring.

Spring constant = ... N/m

[2]

d) State **one** assumption you made to answer part c) ii).

....

[1]

[Total 7 marks]

2   **Figure 1** shows a piece of elastic being stretched between two pieces of wood. The spring
constant of the elastic is 50 N/m and the unstretched length of the elastic is 3.1 cm.

Figure 1

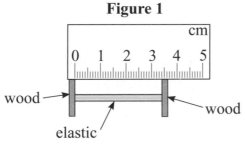

Given that the limit of proportionality hasn't been exceeded,
how much energy is stored in the stretched elastic?

☐ **A** 2.89×10^{-2} J   ☐ **B** 289 J   ☐ **C** 2.25 J   ☐ **D** 2.25×10^{-4} J

[Total 1 mark]

PRACTICAL

Figure 2

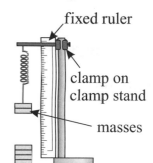

3 A student investigated the relationship between the extension of a spring and the forces acting on it. He hung different weights from the bottom of the spring and measured its extension with a ruler, as shown in **Figure 2**.

Grade 6-7

a) **Figure 3** shows the results that the student obtained in his investigation. Draw the force-extension graph for the student's results on the axes in **Figure 4**.

Figure 3

Force (N)	Extension (cm)
0.0	0.0
1.0	4.4
2.0	7.5
3.0	12.3
4.0	16.0
5.0	22.2
6.0	32.0

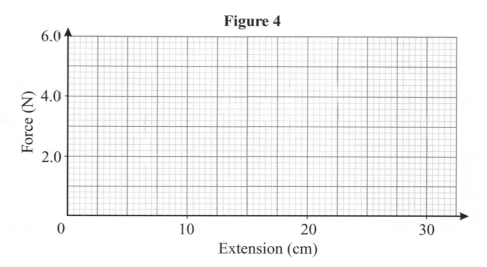

Figure 4

[3]

b) Using the graph you have drawn, calculate the spring constant of the spring being tested.

Spring constant = ... N/m

[2]

c) The student realised he had stretched the spring past its limit of proportionality. Explain how you can tell this from the graph.

....

....

[2]

d) The student removed the masses from the spring. Whilst he unloaded the spring, he measured its extension for each force again. He found that, when unloading the spring, the extension of the spring was 20.1 cm when a force of 4.0 N acted on it. Suggest and explain a reason for this.

....

....

....

[2]

[Total 9 marks]

Exam Practice Tip

It's easy to get caught out by problems like question 2. Remember, for the equations for stretching (or compressing), you need to use the amount the length of an object has changed by, not its total length after it's been stretched.

Biology Mixed Questions

1   Aerobic respiration transfers energy from glucose.   (Grade 4-6)

   a)   i)   Name the subcellular structures where aerobic respiration takes place.

     ....

                                                    [1]

       ii) Complete the word equation for aerobic respiration.

         glucose + ... → .... + water

                                                      [2]

   Glucose is obtained through the diet.

   b)   Once it has passed through the digestive system, glucose is transported around the body in the blood. Name the liquid component of blood.

     ....

                                                    [1]

   c)   Some of the excess glucose from the diet is converted into glycogen and stored in the liver. Explain what happens to this glycogen if the blood glucose concentration falls below normal.

     ....

     ....

                                                    [2]

                                       [Total 6 marks]

2   Alcohol is metabolised in the liver using alcohol dehydrogenase enzymes.   (Grade 4-6)

   a)   One of the functions of the liver is to break down excess amino acids. Which of the following molecules is made up of amino acids?

     ☐   **A**   a carbohydrate

     ☐   **B**   a protein

     ☐   **C**   a lipid

     ☐   **D**   glycerol

                                                    [1]

   b)   Which **one** of the following sentences about enzymes is **true**?

     ☐   **A**   Enzymes speed up chemical reactions in living organisms.

     ☐   **B**   Enzymes are used up in chemical reactions.

     ☐   **C**   Enzymes are products of digestion.

     ☐   **D**   Enzymes are the building blocks of all living organisms.

                                                    [1]

c) A scientist was investigating the effect of temperature on the rate of activity of alcohol dehydrogenase. **Figure 1** shows a graph of his results.

Figure 1

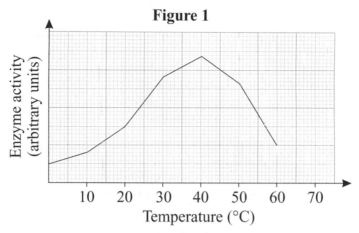

i) What is the optimum temperature for the enzyme? ....

[1]

ii) Suggest and explain the effect a temperature of 70 °C would have on the activity of the enzyme.

....

....

....

[3]

[Total 6 marks]

3   The menstrual cycle is controlled by hormones. **Figure 2** shows the change in the levels of these hormones during one menstrual cycle. It also shows the change in the lining of the uterus.

Grade
6-7

Figure 2

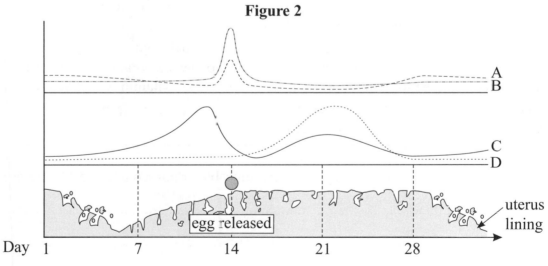

a) i) Which line in **Figure 2** represents oestrogen?

☐ **A**   ☐ **B**   ☐ **C**   ☐ **D**

[1]

ii) Which line in **Figure 2** represents luteinising hormone (LH)?

☐ **A**   ☐ **B**   ☐ **C**   ☐ **D**

[1]

b) Describe how a hormone travels from a gland to its target organ in the body.

....

....
[2]

c) Describe how a high progesterone level affects the secretion of hormones from the pituitary gland.

....

....
[2]

d) Name **two** hormones involved in maintaining the uterus lining.

1. ....

2. ....
[2]

e) State **two** effects of FSH during the menstrual cycle of a woman.

1. ....

2. ....
[2]

[Total 10 marks]

4   Crops can be genetically modified so that they produce substances that they wouldn't normally. An example of this is Golden Rice. Read the information about Golden Rice below.

Grade 6-7

> Golden Rice is a variety of rice that has been genetically modified to produce beta-carotene. Beta-carotene is used in the body to produce vitamin A.
>
> Vitamin A deficiency is a major health problem in some developing countries because many people struggle to get enough beta-carotene and vitamin A in their diet. Golden Rice could be used in these countries to help tackle vitamin A deficiency.
>
> Golden Rice was genetically engineered using a rice plant, a gene from a maize plant and a gene from a soil bacterium.

a) Explain whether vitamin A deficiency is a communicable or non-communicable disease.

....

....
[1]

b) Explain why the genome of Golden Rice will be different to the genome of normal rice.

....

....
[1]

c) Describe the process that may have been used to produce Golden Rice.

....

....

....

....

....

....

....

....

[4]

d) Fertilisers can be added to the soil to help Golden Rice grow.
Explain how fertilisers can help a plant to make proteins.

....

....

....

[2]

[Total 8 marks]

5 Limiting factors affect the rate of photosynthesis.

a) A student was investigating the effect of limiting factors on the rate of photosynthesis
by green algae. The student set up two boiling tubes like the one in **Figure 3**.
She also set up a third tube that did not contain any algae.
The colour of the indicator solution changes as follows:

Figure 3

- At atmospheric CO_2 concentration, the indicator is red.
- At low CO_2 concentrations, the indicator is purple.
- At high CO_2 concentrations, the indicator is yellow.

boiling tube

hydrogencarbonate
indicator

The student covered one of the boiling tubes containing
algae with foil. No light was able to reach the algae in
this tube. All three tubes were left for several hours at a
controlled temperature with a constant light source.
The colour of the indicator solution was then recorded.
The results are shown in **Figure 4**.

algae immobilised
in beads

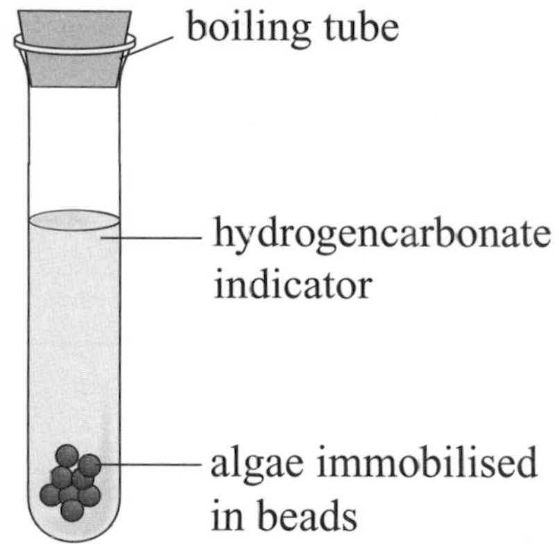

Figure 4

	Algae?	Foil?	Indicator colour at start	Indicator colour at end
Tube 1	yes	yes	red	yellow
Tube 2	yes	no	red	purple
Tube 3	no	no	red	red

i) Name the waste product of photosynthesis.

....

[1]

ii) Name the limiting factor of photosynthesis that is being investigated in this experiment.

....

[1]

iii) Explain the results seen in Tube **1** and Tube **2**.

....

....

....

....

....

....

[4]

iv) Give **two** variables that needed to be controlled in this experiment.

1. ....

2. ....

[2]

b) A scientist investigating the effect of limiting factors on photosynthesis sketched the graph shown in **Figure 5**.

Figure 5

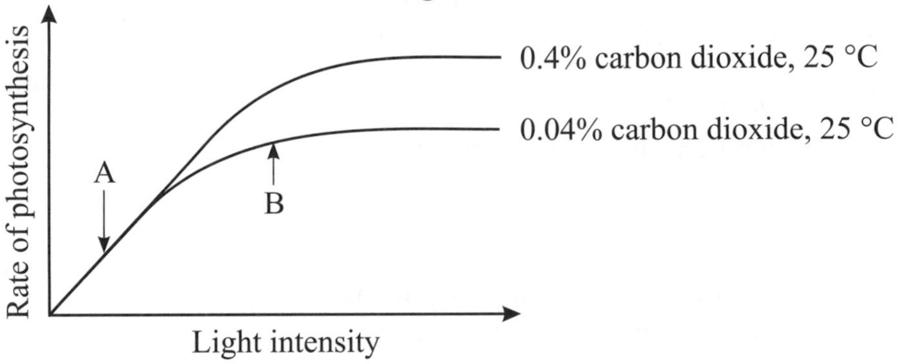

Rate of photosynthesis
Light intensity
0.4% carbon dioxide, 25 °C
0.04% carbon dioxide, 25 °C
A
B

i) Name the limiting factor at point **A**. Explain your answer.

....

....

[2]

ii) Name the limiting factor at point **B**.

....

[1]

[Total 11 marks]

Chemistry Mixed Questions

1 Calcium, Ca, and sulfuric acid, H_2SO_4, react together in a chemical reaction. *(Grade 4-6)*

a) Write a word equation for this reaction.

....
[2]

b) What is the chemical formula of the salt formed by this reaction?

....
[1]

c) Predict whether the salt formed will be soluble or insoluble.

....
[2]

d) The reaction of sulfuric acid with calcium is less violent than its reaction with sodium.
What does this tell you about the position of sodium, relative to calcium, in the reactivity series?

....
[1]

[Total 6 marks]

2 Chlorine is a Group 7 element that exists as molecules of Cl_2. *(Grade 4-6)*

a) Complete **Figure 1** to give a dot-and-cross diagram that shows the bonding in Cl_2.
You only need to show the outer electron shells.

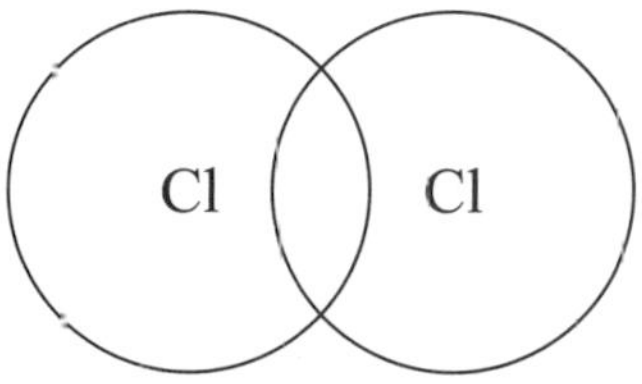

Figure 1
[2]

b) Which of the following **best** describes the structure of chlorine?
Tick **one** box.

☐ **A** Giant ionic lattice   ☐ **C** Simple molecular substance

☐ **B** Giant covalent structure   ☐ **D** Fullerene
[1]

c) Describe a test you could carry out for chlorine. Include any observations you would expect.

....

....
[2]

d) Chlorine has a melting point of −102 °C and a boiling point of −34 °C.
Predict what state chlorine would be in at −50 °C.

....
[1]

[Total 6 marks]

3   Ellie is using paper chromatography experiment to analyse the components in a sample.
     Figure 2 shows the chromatogram produced by the experiment.

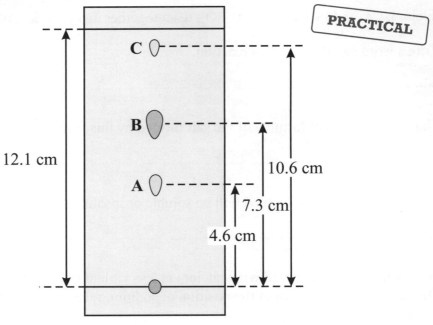

Figure 2

a) Identify the **stationary phase** in Ellie's experiment.

....

[1]

b) Use **Figure 2** to calculate the R_f values for spots **A**, **B**, and **C**.

$$R_f = \frac{\text{distance travelled by solute}}{\text{distance travelled by solvent}}$$

R_f of **A** = ...

R_f of **B** = ...

R_f of **C** = ...

[3]

c) From **Figure 2**, how can you tell that Ellie's sample contains
   a substance that is insoluble in the mobile phase?

....

[1]

d) Use **Figure 2** to identify the **minimum** number of components in Ellie's sample. Tick **one** box.

☐ **A** 1   ☐ **B** 2   ☐ **C** 3   ☐ **D** 4

[1]

e) Ellie concludes that her sample is a mixture. Explain what is meant by the term 'mixture'.

....

....

[1]

f) The mixture contains some liquid components with similar boiling points.
   Name a technique that Ellie could use to separate the different components in the mixture.

....

[1]

[Total 8 marks]

4 Rubidium is an element from Group 1 of the periodic table. Fluorine is an element from Group 7. Rubidium metal, Rb, and fluorine gas, F_2, react violently to produce a single product.

a) Write a balanced symbol equation for the reaction of rubidium metal and fluorine gas.

....

[2]

b) The reaction between rubidium and fluorine is exothermic.
Use the axes in **Figure 3** to draw a reaction profile for the reaction between rubidium and fluorine.

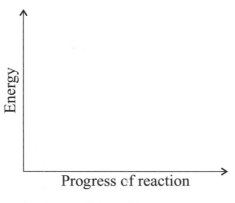

Figure 3

[2]

[Total 4 marks]

5 A student reacts chlorine water reacts with potassium iodide solution according to the following reaction.

$$Cl_{2\ (aq)} + 2KI_{(aq)} \rightarrow 2KCl_{(aq)} + I_{2\ (aq)}$$

a) Chlorine water is corrosive.
State **one** safety precaution that the student should take when carrying out the reaction.

....

[1]

b) Find the relative formula mass of potassium iodide, KI. $A_r(K) = 39$, $A_r(I) = 127$.

....

[1]

c) Describe what the student would observe when he added chlorine water to potassium iodide solution.

....

[1]

d) Explain why this reaction takes place.
Give your answer in terms of the reactivity of the elements involved.

....

....

[2]

e) Write a balanced ionic equation for the reaction between chlorine and potassium iodide.

....

[2]

[Total 7 marks]

Mixed Questions

6 Some elements have several different isotopes. Look at **Figure 4**.
It shows the percentage of the atoms of some elements that exist as each of their isotopes.

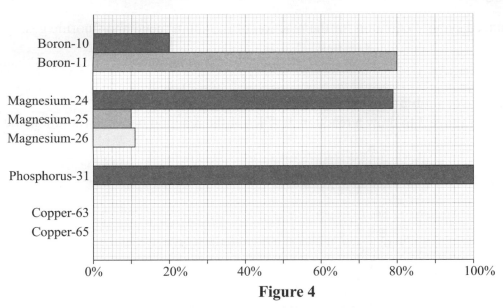

Figure 4

a) 69% of copper atoms are copper-63 and the rest are copper-65.
   Complete **Figure 4** by adding bars for the two isotopes of copper.

[2]

b) Explain why the relative atomic mass of phosphorus is a whole number,
   while the relative atomic masses of boron, magnesium and copper are not.

   ....

   ....

   ....

   ....

   ....

   ....

[3]

c) Use **Figure 4** to calculate the relative atomic mass of magnesium.
   Give your answer to three significant figures.

   relative atomic mass = ...
[4]

[Total 9 marks]

7 A student has a sample of sodium sulfate, Na_2SO_4, with a mass of 34.08 g.
How many oxygen atoms are in the sample, to 4 significant figures?

(relative atomic masses: Na = 23, S = 32, O = 16)

☐ **A** 1.442×10^{23} atoms ☐ **C** 1.015×10^{24} atoms

☐ **B** 5.779×10^{23} atoms ☐ **D** 1.442×10^{24} atoms

[Total 1 mark]

Mixed Questions

8 Aluminium can be obtained by electrolysis of the ore bauxite, Al_2O_3. **Grade 6-7**

The overall equation for this reaction is:

$$2Al_2O_{3\,(l)} \rightarrow 4Al_{(l)} + 3O_{2\,(g)}$$

a) Explain why this reaction is an example of a redox reaction.

....

....

[1]

b) Write a half equation to show the reaction that occurs at the cathode.

....

[2]

c) A scientist carries out an experiment where aluminium oxide is electrolysed.
The scientist starts off with 40.8 g of pure aluminium oxide.
Predict the mass of aluminium she can extract from this mass of electrolyte.
(relative atomic masses: Al = 27, O = 16)

mass = ... g

[4]

d) Iron can be extracted from its ores by heating with carbon.
Explain why this method is **not** suitable for the extraction of aluminium from its ore.

....

....

....

[2]

e) In the UK, some metals are widely recycled. Give **two** advantages of recycling metals.

....

....

[2]

[Total 11 marks]

9 A scientist wants to produce a batch of aluminium sulfate for an experiment.
She plans to do this by reacting aluminium with an excess of sulfuric acid.
A chemical supplier offers three options to provide the quantity of aluminium she needs. **Grade 6-7**

Which of these options will allow the scientist to complete her reaction in the **shortest** time?

☐ **A** 1 aluminium cube with side length 8 cm.

☐ **B** 8 aluminium cubes, each with side length 4 cm.

☐ **C** 64 aluminium cubes, each with side length 2 cm.

☐ **D** They will all take the same length of time.

[Total 1 mark]

Mixed Questions

10 Many different chemical substances are carbon based. (Grade 7-9)

a) Put the carbon based substances butane, diamond and poly(propene) in order of melting point, from **highest** to **lowest**. Explain your answer.

Order: ....

Explanation: ....

....

....

....

[5]

b) Which of the substances from c) i) would be most suitable for using in drill bits? Explain your answer with reference to the bonding in your chosen material.

....

....

....

[3]

[Total 8 marks]

11 A hydrogen-oxygen fuel cell is a type of electrical cell. Hydrogen-oxygen fuel cells can be used to power cars. (Grade 7-9)

a) Hydrogen is the fuel used in the hydrogen-oxygen fuel cell. Suggest **two** advantages associated with using hydrogen as a fuel for cars instead of petrol.

....

....

[2]

b) The reaction that occurs in a hydrogen-oxygen fuel cell is: $2H_2 + O_2 \rightarrow 2H_2O$

Figure 5 shows the energy of the bonds involved in this reaction.

Bond	Bond Energy (kJ mol^{-1})
O=O	498
H–H	436
O–H	463

Figure 5

Calculate the energy change for the reaction which takes place in the hydrogen-oxygen fuel cell.

energy change = ... kJ mol^{-1}

[3]

[Total 5 marks]

Mixed Questions

Physics Mixed Questions

1 A ray of light in a vacuum travels 1 foot in around 1 nanosecond. (Grade 4-6)

a) A foot is a measure of distance. State the SI unit for measuring distance.

....

[1]

b) One nanosecond is equal to

☐ **A** 1×10^9 seconds.   ☐ **C** 1×10^{-6} seconds.

☐ **B** 1×10^{-9} seconds.   ☐ **D** 1×10^{-6} seconds.

[1]

c) Distance and time are both scalar quantities. State what is meant by a scalar quantity.

....

....

[1]

[Total 3 marks]

2 A child pulls a toy along the ground. There is friction between the toy's wheels and the ground. The forces acting on the toy are shown in **Figure 1**. (Grade 4-6)

Figure 1

a) Which of the following shows the correct way to find the resultant force acting on the toy from a scale drawing of the forces acting on it? The dashed lines represent the forces acting on the toy, and the solid line represents the resultant force.

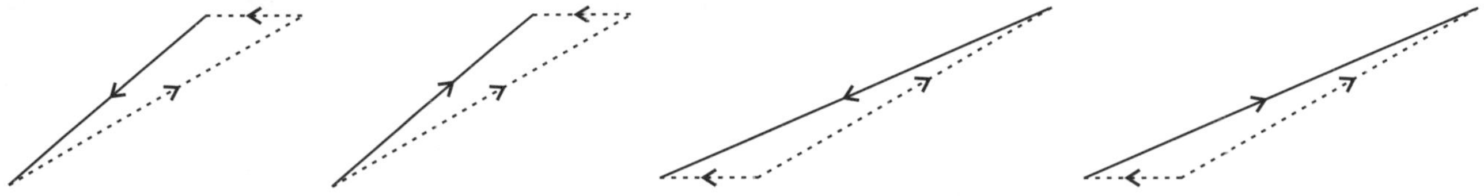

☐ **A**   ☐ **B**   ☐ **C**   ☐ **D**

[1]

b) The total horizontal force acting on the toy is 5 N to the right. Calculate the work done by the child as she pulls it a distance of 10 m to the right. Use the equation:

work done = force × distance moved in the direction of the force.

Work done = ... J

[2]

[Total 3 marks]

A girl is walking her dog. She decides to record the distance she had travelled during the walk every 5 minutes.

a) She uses the information she collected to draw a distance/time graph for her walk. What does the gradient of a distance/time graph represent?

☐ **A** speed

☐ **B** acceleration

☐ **C** distance

☐ **D** deceleration

[1]

b) After exactly 5 minutes, she has walked a distance of 420 m. Calculate the average speed at which she walked. Use the equation:

average speed = distance travelled ÷ time.

Give the unit in your answer.

Average speed = ... Unit: ....

[3]

c) Whilst walking, the girl throws a ball for her dog to chase. Each time she throws the ball, she transfers energy to the ball's kinetic energy store. Which method correctly describes how energy is transferred to the ball?

☐ **A** electrically   ☐ **C** by heating

☐ **B** mechanically   ☐ **D** by radiation

[1]

[Total 5 marks]

---

4   X-rays and gamma rays are types of electromagnetic waves.   (Grade 4-6)

a) Electromagnetic waves are transverse. Give **one** example of a longitudinal wave.

....

[1]

b) State **one** use of each of the following electromagnetic waves.

X-ray: ....

Gamma rays: ....

[2]

c) The equation shows a nucleus emitting a gamma ray. Determine the values of A and B.

$$^{99}_{43}\text{Tc} \rightarrow {}^{A}_{43}\text{Tc} + {}^{B}_{0}\gamma$$

A = ...   B = ...

[2]

[Total 5 marks]

Mixed Questions

5 Radiation is around us all the time. (Grade 6-7)

a) Radioactivity can be measured in different ways.
   Suggest **one** method that could be used to measure the radioactivity of a source.

   ....

   [1]

b) Draw a line from each type of radiation on the left to its correct description on the right.

alpha particle		an electromagnetic wave

beta-minus particle		a helium nucleus

gamma ray		an electron emitted from the nucleus

   [1]

c) Beta decay can also occur through the emission of a beta-plus particle.
   Which of the following statements is **incorrect** for beta-plus decay?

   ☐ **A** A neutron becomes a proton in the nucleus.

   ☐ **B** A positron is emitted from the nucleus.

   ☐ **C** A proton becomes a neutron in the nucleus.

   ☐ **D** The mass number of the nucleus remains the same.

   [1]

d) i) The term 'activity' can be used when describing a radioactive source.
      State what is meant by activity and give the unit it is measured in.

   ....

   [2]

   ii) On the axes in **Figure 2**, sketch how the
       activity of a radioactive source varies over time.

Figure 2

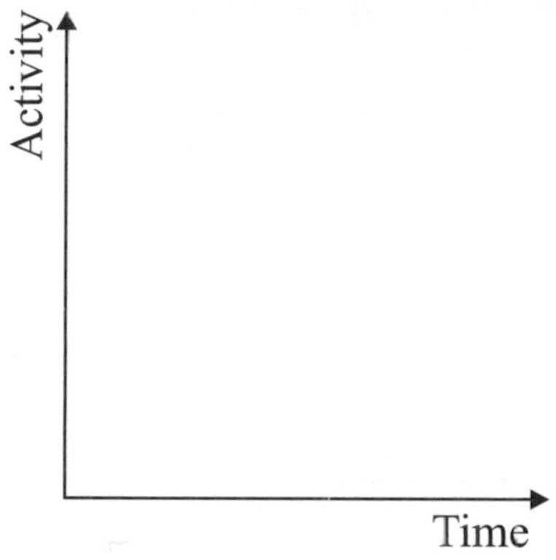

e) The term 'half-life' can also be used when describing a source of radiation.
   State what is meant by half-life. You should refer to activity in your answer.

   ....

   ....

   [1]

   [Total 8 marks]

Mixed Questions

6 A battery powered winch is used to raise a 40.0 kg crate vertically off the ground.

a) Complete **Figure 3** to show the main energy transfers that occur as the crate is lifted.

Figure 3

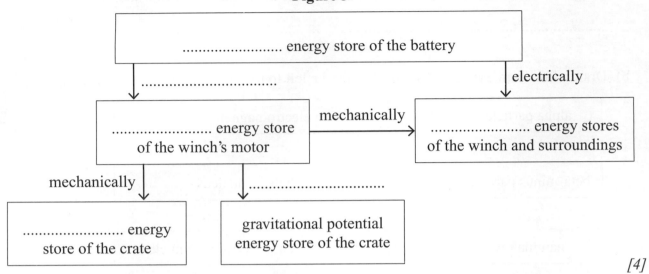

.... energy store of the battery

electrically

....

.... energy store of the winch's motor

mechanically

.... energy stores of the winch and surroundings

mechanically

....

.... energy store of the crate

gravitational potential energy store of the crate

[4]

b) The crate is raised 1.1 m vertically off the ground.
Calculate the energy transferred to the crate's gravitational potential energy store.

Energy transferred = ... J

[4]

[Total 8 marks]

7 Electromagnetic waves are able to travel through a vacuum.

a) i) An infrared wave is travelling through a vacuum. It has a wavelength of 1×10^{-6} m and a frequency of 3×10^{14} Hz. Calculate its speed. Give your answer in standard form.

Speed = ... m/s

[4]

ii) Determine the speed at which radio waves travel in a vacuum.

....

[1]

b) Visible light is another type of electromagnetic wave.
Visible light travels from a vacuum into a glass block, as shown in **Figure 4**. Explain what happens to the wave as it enters and leaves the glass block. In your answer, you should refer to the direction in which the wave is travelling, and its speed.

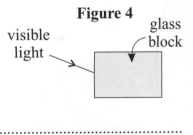

Figure 4

visible light

glass block

....

....

....

....

[4]

[Total 9 marks]

Mixed Questions

8 A student is investigating how the deceleration of a 0.50 kg trolley varies based on the surface it is travelling on. Her set-up is shown in **Figure 5**.

The student uses a spring attached to the wall to provide the driving force for the trolley. She pushes the trolley against the spring until the spring is compressed by 0.040 m each time, then releases it and measures its speed at each light gate.

Figure 5

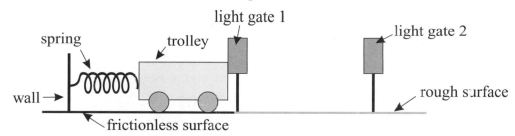

a) State **one** independent variable and **one** dependent variable.

Independent variable: ....

Dependent variable: ....

[2]

b) The table in **Figure 6** shows her results.
Complete the table in **Figure 6** by calculating the magnitude of the acceleration for each repeat.

Figure 6

Repeat	Speed at light gate 1 (m/s)	Speed at light gate 2 (m/s)	Time taken to travel between light gates 1 and 2 (s)	Acceleration (m/s^2)
1	1.22	0.76	2.00	
2	1.16	0.62	2.25	
3	1.19	0.75	2.00	

[3]

Light gate 1 records the trolley's speed just after it leaves the spring. You can assume that no friction acts upon the trolley between it leaving the spring and it passing through light gate 1.

c) Using the information in the table, calculate the energy in the spring's elastic potential energy store when it is compressed. Give your answer to 2 significant figures.

Energy = ... J

[4]

d) The mass of the trolley is 300 g. Use information in the table to calculate the magnitude of the frictional force acting on the trolley.

Force = ... N

[4]

[Total 12 marks]

Mixed Questions

9 A student is designing a basic electronic toy. He wants the toy to be able to light up and spin around. He creates a basic circuit of a battery connected to a motor. In parallel to the motor, he connects two filament bulbs and a fixed resistor. The two bulbs and the resistor are all in series with each other. The bulbs and the motor can be switched on and off separately.

a) Draw the circuit diagram for the circuit created by the student.

[5]

b) The student notices that if the circuit is left on for a long period of time, the resistor and the motor both get hot. Explain the causes of this and suggest **one** way of reducing this heating.

....

....

....

....

....

....

....

[4]

c) The student turns on only the motor. The potential difference across the motor is 6.0 V and a current of 70 mA flows through the motor. After 10 minutes, the student switches off the motor and measures the temperature of the coil of wire inside the motor. He finds that it has increased by 25 °C since it was first turned on.

3.0 g of wire makes up the coil inside the motor.
The material it is made from has a specific heat capacity of 400 J/kg °C.

Calculate the amount of energy that is usefully transferred by the motor in 10 minutes. You can assume that all energy not transferred to thermal energy stores is usefully transferred. Give your answer to 2 significant figures.

Energy transferred usefully = ... J

[5]

[Total 14 marks]

SEHQ41

Mixed Questions